Health and
Safety Education

THE LIBRARY OF EDUCATION

A Project of The Center for Applied Research in Education, Inc.

G. R. Gottschalk, Director

Categories of Coverage

I	II	III
Curriculum and Teaching	Administration, Organization, and Finance	Psychology

IV	V	VI
History, Philosophy, and Social Foundations	Professional Skills	Educational Institutions

Health and
Safety Education

DEOBOLD B. VAN DALEN, *1911-*

Professor of Education
University of Pittsburgh

1963
The Center for Applied Research in Education, Inc.
Washington, D.C.

Foreword

Before undertaking the primary purpose of the monograph, *Health and Safety Education,* Dr. D. B. Van Dalen etches the formative development of health education as essential background for a general understanding of the social significance of health and intelligent health behavior in a democratic society. By design and purpose, the monograph has primary import for those vested with responsibility for helping the young acquire basic insights and knowledge with considerable relevance for continuing learning and long-term utilization.

The role of the school and the facilitation of learning, as well as practice, are presented by the author in convergence of attention upon three dominant features: the structure of learning and knowledge to be apprehended by the student in health and safety education; a complete compatible guide to organization of conducive means appropriate to age level needs and ways of discovering values; the constitution of learning conditions in the environs of both school and community which may best cultivate personal command in exercising self-responsibility for optimum health.

The idea of the significance of good health in the interest of the individual and society is perceptively developed along lines of communication which parallel the student's increasing maturity. Stress is laid on student comprehension of personal assets and requirements and the manner of shaping attitudes likely to affect more positive efforts in dealing with the problems of maintaining health and safety in a complex everyday world.

The monograph, *Health and Safety Education,* alerts the educator to the most difficult task of health education, namely that of merging the boundaries of basic learnings with those of inevitable encounters with life-span demands for intelligent regeneration of health and well being. Thus it lays the causeway between substantive structure and the adaptive enablements of sound planning, interesting instruction and integral evaluation.

MINNIE L. LYNN

v

Contents

CHAPTER VIII

CHAPTER I

The Need for School Health Education

Why provide a health education program in our schools? Can we afford to spend educational dollars for these services? When many pressing needs are vying for attention in the curriculum, can we justify having the staff and student devote time to this program? What do health educators accomplish that is of benefit to children and society?

Strengthening Our Society

Survival—staying alive—is a fundamental goal of man. This yearning was translated into demands for health instruction in the schools about the turn of the century. A narrow conception of health prevailed at first, but gradually, a much fuller image has been brought into focus. To our grandparents, health meant the absence of disease and physical defects; today, it means total fitness for living. Man no longer seeks merely to be unshackled from sickness and infirmity; he aspires to attain optimum physical, mental, social, and emotional wellbeing.

Health has attained a high rank in our heirarchy of values because it provides the keystone for individual and national development. A democratic society values human life and respects the dignity and worth of the individual. It seeks to provide for the fullest development of citizens' capacities so that they can attain maximum personal happiness and make the greatest possible contribution to mankind. This dream cannot be realized unless people enjoy good health. Youths who possess a low level of physical fitness lack the zest for active work and learning. Half-time, half-happy, and half-effective workers experience little satisfaction and success in their school, family, vocational, and community life. Their frustrations, fears, and failures are personal tragedies that can precipitate a national disaster. This nation will not long endure if the American people fail to maintain the physical, mental, and moral vigor that is necessary to strengthen and defend our democratic way of life.

1

The public cannot afford to regard the school health program as an academic fringe benefit, for without it the basic goals of education cannot be fully realized. Of what value is it to provide an academic program for youths if they are physically, socially, and emotionally unable to profit from it? Of what value is it to educate youths if poor health prevents them from fully utilizing their knowledge as adults? The public cannot separate health and education for the body and mind are not separate entities. A child's intellectual attainments are related to his physical wellbeing; his physical condition is affected by his emotions; and his emotions are affected by his school performance and his physical wellbeing. There is a constant, close, deep interrelationship between health and education and between health and individual and national survival.

Health education goals. Educators are well aware of the importance of health. It was placed first in a list of seven desirable objectives to be sought through education by the Commission on the Reorganization of Secondary Education in 1918. Since that time, committees on the national, state, and local levels have repeatedly stipulated that the development of physical and mental health is one of the fundamental purposes of education.

The need for health education becomes more apparent when one notes how it can contribute to the attainment of the general goals of education. In 1938, the Educational Policies Commission crystallized a classic statement of the objectives that youths needed to attain if they were to function effectively as (1) individuals, (2) members of families and groups, (3) as producers and consumers, and (4) as citizens.

The objectives of self-realization. These objectives are concerned with the cultivation of intellectual curiosity and the ability to give responsible direction to one's life. They deal with the acquisition of fundamental skills: reading, writing, speaking, observing, and using numbers. They are concerned with health and recreational knowledges and practices. All teachers can make contributions that will enable youths to experience greater self-realization. Health educators can help them to:

1. Obtain basic knowledge of body structure and function and the interrelationships of the bodily systems;
2. Gain an understanding of the nature and causes of diseases and accidents and methods of preventing and controlling them;

3. Adopt practices that scientific knowledge indicates will protect their lives and improve their health;

4. Understand and accept the influence of heredity on their physical and mental development, cultivate their capacities to peak proficiency, and adjust to their limitations in a manner that enables them to lead satisfying and productive lives;

5. Obtain periodic appraisals of their health status, seek prompt treatment for their disorders and defects, and take protective health measures;

6. Acquire the skills and knowledges to participate effectively in wholesome recreational activities and establish the habit of pursuing them;

7. Establish a healthy regimen of daily living: obtain adequate rest and exercise, eat a well-balanced diet, keep the body and teeth clean, maintain good posture, present a pleasing personal appearance, and establish safe and healthful work and study practices.

The objectives of human relationships.   These objectives stress cultivating a respect for one's fellow man and an appreciation of the importance of the family. They are concerned with the acquisition of homemaking skills and the ability to win friends and to work cooperatively with others. In this area of personal development, health educators can help youths to:

1. Acquire knowledge of the factors that develop and debilitate sound emotional health, appraise their own behavior, and endeavor to establish the most desirable practices;

2. Acquire social and recreational skills that will help them to integrate and enrich family life and establish more extensive and satisfying relationships with others;

3. Develop positive attitudes toward the mentally and physically handicapped;

4. Obtain knowledge concerning the growth patterns, the physical and mental health problems, and the contributions and responsibilities of different age groups and sexes;

5. Establish wholesome relationships with people of various ages and both sexes;

6. Acquire the knowledges and skills necessary to prepare inexpensive but nutritious meals; to render first aid; to provide home nursing care; and to maintain a clean, safe, and healthful home;

7. Make contributions to the solution of family or group health and safety problems and graciously abide by the decisions made.

The objectives of economic efficiency.   These objectives are concerned with the selection of vocations and the acquisition of efficient and effective consumer and producer skills. In this area of development, health educators can help youths to:

1. Obtain knowledge of available vocational opportunities and training programs in the health professions and the qualifications and standards that have been established in each field;

2. Obtain knowledge about the health and safety problems associated with various types of employment;

3. Establish the practice of learning how to perform work in the safest manner and of observing health and safety regulations when on a job;

4. Learn how to obtain and evaluate health information, health services, and health products and establish the practice of choosing them wisely;

5. Make full and intelligent use of health advice and available health facilities and services;

6. Obtain knowledge about the laws and agencies that protect the health of consumers and workers;

7. Form the habit of giving proper consideration to health, food, clothing, and recreation needs when budgeting income.

The objectives of civic responsibility.   These objectives are concerned with the development of attitudes, knowledges, and skills which people need to function as responsible citizens on the local, state and national levels. In this area of development, health educators can help youths to:

1. Assume responsibility for protecting the health of others in daily life and participate in projects designed to improve school and community health, safety, and recreation conditions;

2. Obtain knowledge about the role that the home, school, and health agencies on all governmental levels play in promoting individual and public health;

3. Learn how to locate and evaluate information concerning community health problems and support the proposals that will be of the greatest benefit to mankind;

4. Recognize the interdependence of all people in relation to the maintenance of health and the control of disease and accidents;

5. Obtain knowledge about the existing inequalities in human living conditions and health status throughout the world and support efforts to improve them;

6. Develop a positive attitude toward applying scientific findings that will improve the health and wellbeing of mankind and actively oppose practices that will be harmful to the moral or physical status of human beings;

7. Obtain knowledge concerning the laws and regulations that pertain to health, safety, and recreation and obey them.

Solving Our Health Problems

The preceding discussion suggests some of the objectives that the health education program has strived to achieve. To determine what role the program should play in the future, two questions must be raised: Has it helped the American people solve their health problems? What problems persist and what new ones have arisen that require attention?

Past accomplishments. A momentary look into the past reveals that death and disease have been star players in the pageant of community life. Tombstones in older cemeteries stand as grim reminders of the terrifying epidemics of smallpox, typhoid, cholera, and diphtheria that periodically swept across the nation. Other stone slabs tell tragic tales of sudden deaths in factory, farm, and mine accidents. Scores of graves supply silent testimony to the hazards that were associated with childbirth and infancy.

A glance at current statistical reports indicate a sharply falling death rate. Striking decreases in the death rates for influenza and pneumonia can be noted. The downtrend in infant, maternal, and child mortality rates during the past sixty years has been remarkable. Typhoid fever and diphtheria, which were major causes of death in 1900, are now of negligible numerical significance. Smallpox has been almost eradicated. Tuberculosis no longer appears among the first ten important causes of death. Poliomyelitis appears to be on the wane and deaths from venereal diseases are down. Growth studies reveal that our children are taller and heavier than those of previous generations. Since the turn of the century, life expectancy has increased almost twenty years! This astonishing record has been made possible by the discovery of immunization procedures and new drugs, the passage of public health measures, the advance in medical knowledge and skills, and the rise in our standard of living. The health education provided in the schools also deserves a large share of credit for the tremendous progress that has taken place.

Present problems. Although great advances have been made in improving health and prolonging life during this century, even greater challenges await us. Because of the recent population explosion, our nation must redouble its efforts to improve child health. Good health habits must be established early in life: once undesirable health habits are established, it is extremely difficult to eradicate them. The sooner youths can be acquainted with the principles of healthful living, the more likely they are to apply them. The earlier preventive and protective health measures can be provided, the more effectively future drains on our financial and human resources can be eliminated. As medicine conquers one disease, it must march on to overcome others. As researchers keep pouring forth more sophisticated findings, educators must quickly disseminate the information and get youths to apply it in their daily lives. In this era of promised prolongation of life, educators must help students to acquire a sound foundation for meeting the health problems of later life. In this century of ideological competition, our democratic society must strive to minimize the difference in death rates among different races, sexes, economic groups, and geographical regions. In this Atomic-Space Age, when men venture into outer space and toy with awesome forces that can destroy all mankind, health can no longer be considered merely a local problem. There is little place in society for the physically and mentally "marginal" man. The nation simply will not survive if an all-out effort is not made to conserve and cultivate our human resources.

Diseases and illnesses.   Despite our decreasing morbidity and mortality rates, disease is still the major cause of disability and death in the United States. Heart disease is the principal cause of death; cancer is second. These diseases are most commonly associated with the middle years and old age, but they also take their toll among children. Rheumatic fever and rheumatic heart disease are common enemies in childhood. In the 5–14 and 15–24 age groups, heart diseases rank fifth among the causes of death. Cancer ranks fourth as the cause of death in the 1–4 age group and second in the 5–14 and 15–24 age groups.

Poliomyelitis, tuberculosis, and many communicable diseases appear to be under control, but periodic outbreaks are a sharp reminder that persistent vigilance is required to maintain that control. The rise of venereal diseases among teenagers has become a source of concern. Respiratory infections keep the average American away from school or work several days each year. The common cold is one of the most frequent causes of disabling illnesses among children and secondary infections often follow, resulting in pneumonia, bronchitis, sinusitis, and infections of the middle ear. Childhood diseases are common but none of them are now of major importance as causes of death.

Accidents and injuries.   Accidents are the leading cause of death among schoolchildren. Motor vehicles, drownings, fires, and explosives, and firearms account for most of the accidental deaths. The death rate is considerably higher for boys than it is for girls. Death rates, however, do not tell the whole story: for every child that is killed, many more are hurt and physically disfigured or disabled. These conditions make it imperative for health educators to help youngsters acquire safe living skills and practices and for schools to provide the safeguards and supervision necessary to prevent accidents.

Physical exercise.   Because of advances in technology, shifts in social status symbols, and the rise in the standard of living, many modern youngsters fail to obtain sufficient physical exercise: they ride rather than walk; watch television in darkened rooms rather than play in the sunshine; press buttons to operate labor-saving devices rather than contract muscles to perform physically demanding chores. This lack of bodily activity presents a serious threat to our society. Well-supervised physical education programs could go a long way toward developing healthy, happy youths.

Nutrition.   Surveys of food consumption in our affluent society reveal that many people are malnourished. Studies of underweight children indicate that the availability of food often is not the cause of their condition. The conspicuous presence of carious teeth, obesity, dietary fads, and pills to relieve constipation or remove excess weight reveal that people do not have an intelligent understanding of the kinds and quantities of food that are required to maintain good health. Schools can perform a valuable service by offering students sound nutritional guidance.

Physical defects.   Physical defects keep many students from making satisfactory social, emotional, and scholastic adjustments. The most common defects are poor vision (including blindness), speech and hearing impairments, and orthopedic and dental defects. Since the inception of the school health program, steady progress has been made in correcting and preventing these conditions. During the past decade, particularly, the programs for handicapped youngsters have been greatly expanded. Nevertheless, school and military health records continue to reveal a high incidence of correctable physical defects. Educators, therefore, must intensify their effort to help youths detect and correct such problems. They must inform pupils about preventive practices, acquaint them with available services, help them obtain proper care, and assist them in adjusting to irremedial defects.

Consumer efficiency.   In the pursuit of health, millions of dollars are spent each year for useless or dangerous medicines, tonics, pills, gadgets, and preparations of various kinds. Thousands of sufferers succumb to the solicitations of medical quacks. Obviously, some segments of the public lack the health information that is necessary to protect themselves from the loss of their money and, possibly, their lives. Alerting our children to these existing dangers is an important responsibility for health educators to assume.

Emotional and social adjustment.   It is difficult to ascertain how many schoolchildren are emotionally disturbed, but certainly mental disease constitutes a major health problem. Mental patients occupy approximately half of the hospital beds in the United States. Homicide and suicide rank as the third and fourth leading causes of death in the 15–24 age group. Emotional problems prevent many youngsters from making satisfactory progress in school and adult life and they often lead to juvenile crime, alcoholism, drug addiction, divorce, fatal accidents, and suicide. The desirable school program should provide for detection and correction of emotional problems.

Many of the health problems that persist today cannot be solved by doing things for people; they must be solved by the people *themselves.* Obesity, accidents, alcoholism, and many other alarming conditions are caused by faulty personal habits and cannot be eradicated unless individuals understand the nature of the problems and assume responsibility for correcting their practices. Education rather than legislation is the major force that is needed to bring about many health improvements in the nation.

Because the school reaches all children for several years, it can disseminate health information more effectively and more economically than many other agencies. The school has the time and the staff available to provide a coordinated, long-term health program and it can mobilize quickly to meet emergency situations. Health educators are trained to work with children and to supply correct, up-to-date information. They are equipped to support and supplement the health effort made by parents, doctors, dentists, and local health agencies. Thus, the school can serve as a catalyst in the community health effort and insure greater success in the overall health program.

CHAPTER II

Evolvement of the School Health Program

The complex school health program can best be understood by examining the historical and cultural forces that brought it into being.[1] The first seeds were planted in the nineteenth century when exciting scientific and economic revolutions focused the nation's attention upon health problems. With the rise of industrialization and immigration, cities swelled with waves of immigrants and former farm workers, diseases thrived in crowded tenements, and factory accidents took their toll of human lives. In 1850, the *Report of the Sanitary Commission of Massachusetts* presented a comprehensive statement of the country's health needs. This report did not spark an immediate reform movement, but crusading journalists and social workers kept hammering the American people with stories and statistics concerning epidemics, sewage and garbage disposal, safe water supply, food inspection, and moral problems.

When the dramatic germ theories of Pasteur, Lister, Koch, and others provided medical men with the knowledge necessary to control communicable diseases, the public began to take action. Governmental authorities on all levels established health agencies. Sweeping measures for improving public sanitation were passed. Captains of industry poured fabulous fortunes into foundations to promote human betterment. Laymen organized several voluntary health bodies: National Tuberculosis Association (1904), Society for Sanitary and Moral Prophylaxis (1905), National Committee for Mental Hygiene (1909), American Cancer Society (1913), National Safety Council (1913), American Social Hygiene Association (1914), and many others.

By the twentieth century, the American people had become convinced that disease and poverty were not inevitable and that the welfare of the nation could be improved through public instruction. Consequently, the health movement swept into educational institu-

---

[1] Richard K. Means, *A History of Health Education in the United States* (Philadelphia: Lea and Febiger, 1962).

tions, and within a few decades leaders had molded a program consisting of three divisions: (1) health instruction, (2) health services, and (3) healthful school living.

School Health Education

Early American teachers were primarily concerned with the mind, rather than the body, of the child, but between 1830 and 1880 a small wave of sentiment favoring the promotion of physical fitness rippled through educational circles. During these years, a few schools introduced calisthenics and gymnastics and courses in physiology and hygiene, and in the 1880's a number of other institutions followed their example. For the most part, however, health education has been a development of the twentieth century.

Formation of the program. The vigorous leadership of many different men and organizations brought the school health program into being. In the 1830's, when physicians advocated that the schools introduce the study of physiology, Horace Mann launched a campaign to put their advice into practice. On platforms and in publications, the father of the common school movement eloquently urged administrators to place hygiene in the "first rank after the elementary branches" of learning and dramatically proclaimed that nobody was qualified to teach a single day who was ignorant of the principles of physiology. His campaign achieved a prominent place for hygiene in the first public normal school in 1839. The *Sixth Annual Report of the Massachusetts Board of Education,* which Mann devoted primarily to the problem of health instruction, gave further impetus to the movement. Another milestone was reached in 1850 when Massachusetts made the teaching of physiology mandatory.

During the 1880's, physiology and hygiene entered the public schools in the wake of the Women's Christian Temperance Union movement. By 1890, the powerful pressures exerted by the WCTU had resulted in the passage of laws by every state requiring schools to teach about the dangers of alcohol and narcotics. When administrators began to comply with these laws, publishers produced hygiene books that incorporated these materials. This marked the beginning of health instruction on a broad scale.

Many factors converged after 1900 that forced an expansion of this movement. Leaders of the new health organizations thought that they could change health practices most quickly by working through the schools. Between 1908 and 1910, for example, members of the National Tuberculosis Association persuaded twenty-eight states to pass legislation requiring schools to provide instruction concerning tuberculosis. With the convening of the first White House Conference on Child Health and Protection in 1910 and the creation of the United States Children's Bureau in 1912, the health needs of youth came under closer scrutiny.

About this time some educational philosophers began to advocate that teachers focus attention on the total development of the child. Their advice did not go unheeded. As early as 1910, Dr. Thomas D. Wood and other leaders drafted a new health program which was published in the *Ninth Yearbook* of the National Society for the Study of Education. The physical education, health inspection, and home economic programs that were introduced during these years gave added impetus to the health movement. Health gained a firmer foothold in the curriculum in 1918 when it was listed among the seven cardinal objectives of education. When the shocking statistics concerning the physical unfitness of World War I draftees were published, the American people were thoroughly aroused and prodded politicians until legislatures broke out with a rash of bills to make health education compulsory.

Many schools immediately introduced health programs, but some administrators made no more than a pretense of complying with the law by having physical educators give "hygiene" talks on rainy days. Health organizations became alarmed about these conditions and rallied their forces to hasten the adoption and improvement of health instruction. The Joint Committee on Health Problems in Education of the American Medical Association and the National Education Association, which was organized in 1911, provided outstanding services. The American Child Health Association and numerous other voluntary agencies and foundations were also active. These organizations financed surveys, conducted demonstrations, promoted studies, printed information, contributed to the improvement of teaching, and promoted cooperation between public health forces.

A number of people, foundations, and agencies played a part in expanding the movement. In the 1920's and 1930's, C. E. Turner and others conducted well-publicized experiments which demonstrated that health education could change pupil behavior. In 1937, the American Association for Health, Physical Education, and Recreation incorporated "Health" in its present title to satisfy members who were enthusiastic workers in the field. The American Public Health Association first established educational qualifications for school health educators in 1938. Participants at the 1930 White House Conference analyzed youths' health needs, evaluated the progress that had been made, and compiled comprehensive lists of recommendations for public and private agencies in the field.

The depression of the 1930's temporarily halted the expansion of school health programs, but the movement regained momentum as soon as economic conditions improved. When World War II again focused the nation's attention on health, governmental and professional agencies quickly appointed national committees to publish materials that would help schools promote physical fitness through health education. Although considerable progress had been made by mid-century, 34 per cent of the high school students and 7 per cent of the elementary school children still received no regular health instruction.[2] Renewed efforts to improve the health of youths were made in 1956, when President Eisenhower called the National Conference on Fitness of American Youth. This led to the creation of the cabinet-level President's Council on Youth Fitness and the President's Citizens Advisory Committee on the Fitness of American Youth. President Kennedy took steps to further this program when he took office.

Objectives. Early in this century, masses of health facts were funneled into students, but these kernels of knowledge did not always bear fruit. The possession of information about health did not automatically change personal and community behavior. After World War I, to correct this situation, teachers began to shift some of their attention from the acquisition of knowledge to its application. Motivating youngsters to improve specific health habits, skills, attitudes, and understandings remains a major objective of educators today. Moreover, since the 1930's, emphasis has been placed upon developing critical thinking skills that will help pupils solve

---

[2] National Education Association, Research Division, "Personnel and Relationships in School Health, Physical Education, and Recreation," *Research Bulletin of the NEA,* 23 (October, 1950), 83.

health problems whenever they arise in our ever-changing society.

Methods. As educators revised their objectives, they revolutionized their teaching methods. In the early physiology and hygiene courses, the emphasis was on transmitting knowledge; teachers delivered dire warnings concerning injurious habits of living, crammed lectures with negative health rules, and had students memorize masses of abstract facts about the body and diseases. After the turn of the century, men who had become acquainted with the work of Pestalozzi, Froebel, Herbart, Hall, and Dewey severely criticized these practices. These leaders urged health educators to take a more positive approach toward instruction and to link learning experiences more closely with children's immediate needs and natural interests.

This advice inspired many teachers to experiment with new ways of enlivening their classes. Toothbrush drills, games, and plays became popular. Health slogans, such as "Drink six glasses of water a day" and "A clean tooth never decays" appeared in classrooms. When the Tuberculosis Association initiated the Modern Health Crusade in 1915, six million students became "crusaders" who fought disease by performing eleven health habits daily. Many youngsters also participated in The Rules of the Game, a project sponsored by the Child Health Organization.

Some of the new teaching techniques were successful; others were not. Educators soon discovered that competitive contests, awards, and badges tended to encourage dishonesty and did not always produce beneficial long-term results. Consequently, external means of motivating pupils were gradually abandoned and a search was made for other ways of capturing interest. During the 1920's and 1930's, a concentrated effort was made to find ways of giving insights into basic health principles that would make youths want to cultivate good habits for their own benefit. To achieve this objective, curriculum committees examined courses of study and weeded out adult-accumulated information that had little relation to the pupils' own experiences. They surveyed youths' health needs and interests and designed curriculums consisting of learning experiences that would fill these needs and guide these interests.

Since the 1930's, the old, pedantic, formal, single-textbook "telling and testing" type of instruction has been disappearing. It is being replaced by large, integrated units of work that require students to solve personal, home, school, and community health and safety problems that directly concern them. In addition to their textbooks, students now explore a variety of other resource materials in the school and community. While collecting, analyzing, and evaluating data to solve their problems, they gain meaningful understanding of health principles and practice in applying them. As a result, they not only acquire habits that will prove useful in similar situations, but also develop critical thinking behavior that will enable them to deal more effectively with future health problems.

Curriculum.   The modern health curriculum bears little resemblance to those constructed in the nineteenth century. Twenty-five hygiene books were on the market by 1860, and the first graded texts appeared in 1884. But most of the early textbooks were written by physicians who tended to produce watered-down versions of volumes they themselves had studied. Thereafter, an increasing number of books were written by nonmedical men. They described the nervous, skeletal, alimentary, respiratory, and circulatory systems, and some of them commented on the dangers of corset lacing. After 1880, many authors attempted to satisfy the demands of the influential WCTU by devoting almost half of their discussions to the evils of smoking and drinking.

During the first two decades of the twentieth century, educational leaders re-evaluated the curriculum—adding, criticizing, and exchanging ideas on how to improve it. About 1918, the term *health education* was introduced to describe the new and more comprehensive concept of instruction. When schools adopted this type of program, administrators erased the old terms, *physiology* and *hygiene,* from their schedules and referred to their new programs as *health education.*

Down through the years, scientific and social changes have made educators add many health topics to the curriculum. Because of the advances in medical science, they began to devote less time to body structure and functions after 1900 and more time to personal and public health and the prevention of communicable diseases. Modern textbooks contain almost twice as much material on food and nutrition as appeared in earlier books. In recent decades, a great effort has been made to link instruction with the overall school and community health program. Today, teachers engage in much more individual counseling than their predecessors did. High-pressure advertising and the multiplicity of health products on the market have forced them to provide more consumer education. Considerable material on mental hygiene has been added to courses and many schools have introduced units concerning growth and development and the elements of wholesome family life and sex education.

The amount of safety instruction in the curriculum has steadily increased since World War I. As early as 1913, the National Safety Council advocated that schools provide safety education—a topic that was almost ignored in the existing textbooks. In the 1920's, pioneer programs were initiated in St. Louis, Detroit, and Kansas City. In 1930, interested organizations established rules for the school boy patrols that had sprung up with the advent of automobiles. Many schools organized junior safety councils after Rochester, New York, set the example in 1918. Driver training courses, which were introduced in the 1930's, multiplied rapidly after World War II.

Teacher Preparation.   When the first state health instruction laws were passed, administrators drafted physical educators, home economists, nurses, science majors, or anyone who was available to teach the courses. Some of these pioneers took an intense interest in the work, others lacked preparation in the field and resented being pressed into service. A number of agencies came to the aid of teachers who were struggling to establish health programs. The American Child Health Association sponsored demonstrations, research studies, and conferences. The American National Red Cross, which provided first aid programs for laymen in 1903, began to train public school teachers. In 1924, the Joint Committee on Health Problems in Education of the American Medical Association and the National Education Association published *Health Education: A Program for Public Schools and Teacher Training Institutions.* This volume, which has since been revised five times, has had a tremendous influence on the school health movement.

Although much progress has been made, mid-century studies reveal that the health education of most classroom teachers and many health instructors has been deficient. To remedy this situation, some states have made health education a certificate requirement for all teacher candidates and have established special standards for health majors. Professional groups have compiled several reports

outlining the desirable competencies and areas of education that
institutions should provide for the preparation of all teachers, health
majors, physical education majors, and students pursuing graduate
health programs.[3]

With these guides available to help them, colleges have made a
tremendous effort to develop better preparatory programs. In recent
decades, they have rejuvenated their traditional health lectures for
all prospective teachers by reducing the size of classes, expanding
the program, and probing personal and professional problems that
are of vital concern to the participants. The number of institutions
offering major programs in health education almost doubled between 1950 and 1960. One report indicates that at least 67 institutions offer undergraduate major programs in health education and
32 of these also offer graduate programs; 161 institutions offer
comprehensive undergraduate programs in health and physical education and 60 of these also offer graduate programs.[4] In-service
programs have also become popular as a means of improving the
health preparation of teachers. Throughout the nation instructors
attend workshops, engage in curriculum revisions, participate in
pilot and demonstration studies, and serve on health councils.

The postgraduate regional institutes that were held in 1961 to
acquaint teachers with the latest health research findings had a favorable reception. Information and assistance in developing similar
institutes can be obtained from the sponsoring agencies: The American Association for Health, Physical Education and Recreation
and the School Health Section of the United States Public Health
Service (Department of Health, Education, and Welfare).

Healthful School Living

Students are affected by their school environment. Consequently,
in addition to health education classes, educators have developed

[3] Fred V. Hein, "Health Education," *Encyclopedia of Educational Research*
(New York: The Macmillan Company, 1960), 629; H. F. Kilander, ed., *Preparing
the Health Teacher* (Washington, D.C.: American Association for Health, Physical
Education, and Recreation, 1961); Report of the Professional Preparation Con-
ference, *Professional Preparations in Health Education, Physical Education,
Recreation Education* (Washington, D.C.: American Association for Health,
Physical Education, and Recreation, 1962).

[4] "NCATE Accredited Institutions Offering Health Degrees in Health, Physical
Education, Recreation," *Journal of Health, Physical Education, and Recreation,* 32
(May–June 1962), 45.

a healthful school living program. Through this program they endeavor to provide for a "safe and healthful environment, the organization of a healthful school day, and the establishment of interpersonal relationships favorable to the best emotional, social, and physical health of pupils."[5]

School buildings.   Healthful school living depends in large part on the physical structure of the building. The old one-room schoolhouse may evoke fond memories, but the community drinking dipper, the pail of untested water, and the unsanitary toilet facilities did not make positive contributions to students' health. Horrendous hazards existed in many nineteenth century city schools. The narrow halls and central staircases in the three- and four-story wooden structures often served as disastrous firetraps. Dark and depressing classrooms, smelly corridors, and inadequate heating facilities created an unpleasant learning environment. When physical education crept into the curriculum, some schools had no playgrounds. Administrators converted halls and basements into gymnasiums, but they rarely made provisions for showers and dressing rooms. After 1900, most school boards began to construct new buildings of brick rather than of wood and some directed architects to include gymnasiums and swimming pools in their plans.

The population explosions that followed World Wars I and II precipitated school construction booms. Moreover, in the period between the two wars, many laws were passed, standards were established, and research studies were conducted that led to the selection of more suitable school sites and the construction of safer and more attractive buildings. The flexible, one-floor plan probably is the most popular today. The construction of a central unit with extended wings makes it possible to separate areas of quiet and noisy activities. Spacious windows, wide halls, pleasing color schemes, and furnishings that are suitable for the age and size of the pupils are found in most new buildings. Many of them contain gymnasiums, swimming pools, showers, locker rooms, and health suites and are surrounded by well-landscaped recreation areas that are used by classes and the entire community. These schools are practically fireproof, but fire alarm systems, extinguishers, and regular fire drills give an added measure of protection. The provisions made

---

[5] "Report of the Committee on Terminology in School Health Education," *Journal of Health, Physical Education, and Recreation,* 22 (September, 1951), 14.

for heating, lighting, acoustics, water supply, and waste disposal conform to the highest health and safety standards. A corps of custodians, some of whom have had special training, keep the premises safe, sanitary, and spotlessly clean.

Lunch programs.   School feeding programs for undernourished children were launched early in the century and mid-morning milk periods also became commonplace. Cafeterias first appeared in the high schools, but with the advent of more working mothers and consolidated schools, elementary schools soon found it necessary to provide noon lunches. Volunteers established many of the early programs in dingy basement rooms where students gulped hurried lunches amidst litter, noise, and unsanitary conditions. Because of the persistent efforts of parents and educators, most pupils now eat in attractive cafeterias that meet the highest hygienic standards. Sufficient time is allotted for a leisurely meal which is low in cost and free to those who cannot afford to pay. Many school boards employ dieticians to manage the cafeterias and supervise all other cafeteria workers. Teachers capitalize on the instructional opportunities that cafeterias offer: in this real-life laboratory they help children select well-balanced meals, develop good eating habits, and acquire the social skills that provide for healthful and happy mealtime experiences.

Teachers and program.   Victorian school directors thoroughly investigated the moral character of prospective employees but paid little heed to their physical and emotional fitness. Today, school boards know that ailing and absent teachers have an unfavorable influence on children; hence, they endeavor to obtain staff members who possess glowing health, abundant vitality, and a wholesome outlook on life. Moreover, many of them require employees to take annual physical examinations.

The health of students is affected not only by the physical fitness, but also by the personality, health habits, and instructional methods of a teacher. Hence, when modern administrators evaluate a prospective employee, they pose some of the following questions: Is he objective and firm but good-natured and friendly when working with students? When planning lessons and activities does he give consideration to the age level, home background, visual difficulties, and health problems of pupils? Does he alternate sedentary pursuits and physical activities? Does he employ instructional techniques that keep noise, tension, and confusion at a minimum? Does he observe sound health and safety practices and motivate children to follow his example? Does he gear classwork and homework to the physical and mental capacities of pupils and protect them from excessive worry and fatigue? Does he create a stimulating, attractive learning climate in which every child strives for peak performance, experiences the joy of personal achievement and social acceptance, and meets failures realistically?

School day.   Many conditions aside from the quality of the staff and building can affect the health of pupils: double sessions, large classes, a rapid turnover of staff members, hallway stampedes, crammed schedules, and long rides in packed, noisy, unsafe buses. Administrators are coping successfully with some staff, space, and double-shift problems. They are employing more health and guidance counselors to help students select academic and extracurricular activities and make a wholesome adjustment to school life. Current pressures that are being exerted to raise academic standards, lengthen the school day, and extend the school year raise new questions that administrators must answer: Will a proposed policy have a deleterious affect on children? What precautions should be taken to protect the health of pupils when a new plan is adopted?

School Health Services

The health service staff members who are responsible for the third aspect of the school health program "(a) appraise the health status of pupils and school personnel; (b) counsel pupils, parents, and other persons involved, concerning appraisal findings; (c) encourage the correction of remediable defects; (d) help plan for the health care and education of handicapped children; (e) help prevent and control disease; (f) provide emergency care for the sick and injured."[6]

Introduction of inspection programs.   France initiated the school health inspection movement in the 1830's and several European countries followed her example. In the United States, Dr. William Alcott recommended as early as 1840 that the schools ought to have physicians, but his suggestions were largely ignored. In the 1890's, serious epidemics finally prompted communities to act, and

---
[6] *Ibid.,* p. 14.

when the emergencies were over some school systems retained the doctors. By 1911, over four hundred cities provided medical inspection in the schools. The school doctors, who were usually obtained from the local board of health, served as sanitary policemen: They excluded ill students from school, examined them when they returned, vaccinated those who could not afford family physicians, and made incidental examinations of the school sanitary facilities.

When the passage of compulsory education laws (1850–1918) opened the schools to children from all segments of society, the existing health programs could not begin to cope with all the problems. Teachers and doctors were appalled when they noted the number of pupils suffering from malnutrition, deafness, impaired vision, orthopedic defects, skin disorders, head lice, and decayed teeth. Little study was needed to discover that these conditions were often responsible for truancy, poor scholarship, and absence. Consequently, educators and physicians quickly joined forces and urged the public to provide for more comprehensive school health services.

These campaigns brought results. In 1899, Connecticut passed legislation that instituted vision testing; in 1903, New Jersey required a complete physical examination; in 1904, Vermont made ear, eye, and throat examinations compulsory. In 1912, New York City employed a school nurse on a trial basis. Reading, Pennsylvania, appointed the first school dentist in 1903; Bridgeport, Connecticut, added dental hygienists to the staff in 1914; and in 1909 Cleveland opened a dental clinic for children whose parents could not afford private medical service. Some cities provided fresh-air activities and rest periods for undernourished children. Early in the century, a few dedicated workers launched programs to help handicapped youngsters. The buildings and equipment they obtained were inadequate, but the principle was established that schools should provide educational opportunities for such pupils.

These pioneer programs did not immediately become a universal phenomenon. In 1910, only about half of the school children in the country received physical examinations, and many of these examinations were conducted by nurses. Because their personnel was limited, schools conducted perfunctory health examinations, kept few records, and did little follow-up work. Some segments of the public were opposed to the new programs, particularly those parents who thought that schools were infringing on their rights, physicians who feared these services would undermine private practice, citizens who objected to additional taxation, and teachers who disliked added duties.

Growth of health service programs.   Reports of the astounding number of physically unfit World War I draftees spurred many schools to expand their health services. Athletic associations began to require rigid physical examinations for all varsity athletes. An increasing number of doctors, nurses, and dentists joined school staffs. Those who were fortunate enough to serve in new buildings often found health suites awaiting them with examining rooms, restrooms, offices, and perhaps a clinic. Throughout the nation, school lunch programs were improved; better procedures for immunization were established; and provisions were made for accident prevention and the emergency care of the sick and injured. Because the old title, *health inspection,* did not satisfactorily describe the new and more comprehensive programs, educators dropped the term in the 1920's and substituted the more suitable title *health services.*

In 1930, a call for further progress was sounded at the White House Conference, and participants pledged that every child should receive health protection from birth through adolescence. Hope for achieving this goal dwindled in the depression decade that followed when many schools were obliged to reduce drastically their health services. But the distressing economic conditions focused national attention upon poverty and disease, and public sentiment soon forced the federal government to assume a greater responsibility for citizens' health. As a result, various branches of the government initiated health surveys; the 1935 Social Security Act gave aid to the states for maternal and child health and crippled children; the school lunch program was established on a temporary basis in 1935 and was placed on a permanent basis in 1946; and the National Mental Health Act of 1946 extended mental health services.

By mid-century, health service programs were well established in public schools. Continual vigilance had brought many communicable diseases almost completely under control, and schools were able to devote more time to other problems. In the past few decades, many schools have added psychologists and other specialists to their staffs, and as a result better provisions are now made for improving mental health and caring for exceptional children. Since World War II, a number of well-equipped classrooms for these youngsters have been put into service, and many colleges have developed or expanded teacher preparatory programs in this field. Today, doctors and dentists still serve too many students, but the number of school nurses is approaching the standards suggested by authorities.

Because of the shortage of school doctors, many schools have abandoned the practice of conducting annual examinations and follow instead the recommendations of the American School Health Association and the American Medical Association by arranging for four to five medical examinations during the school life of the child and providing special examinations whenever necessary. Parents are often invited to be present and the examinations are considerably more complete than they once were. The emotional and social behavior of the student, as well as his physical condition, are appraised. Staff members keep simple, accurate, cumulative records of health appraisals, home visits, and conferences, and make them accessible to school personnel. Doctors, nurses, and dentists endeavor to make their contacts with children and parents educative experiences. In letters and conferences they interpret appraisal findings to pupils and parents, counsel them concerning corrective and preventive measures, and suggest how to adjust to conditions that cannot be remedied. Over the years, school health workers have shifted their emphasis from "correction to prevention, from diagnosis to education and referral, from the sterile amassing of records of findings to the interpretation and follow-through for the child's benefit."[7] They have labored to improve public relations and to coordinate school and community health services. Mutual agreements have been made with local medical societies and public health officers concerning the nature of school procedures and the extent of the services offered. Through professional organizations, workers have produced publications to guide schools in the development of health service programs. Educators can be proud of the progress that has been made in the past half-century, but much work remains to be done.

---

[7] Marie A. Hinrichs, "Health Services—Elementary and Secondary," *Encyclopedia of Educational Research* (New York: The Macmillan Company, 1960), p. 641.

CHAPTER III

The Organization of
the Health and Safety Program

Levels of Organization

Our nation is committed to the proposition that improving the health of youth is a major objective of education. A vast army of workers has been organized to translate this belief into practice. The states and the local school districts assume much of the responsibility, but they receive assistance from many other sources.[1] Thousands of health agencies now exist on the international, national, state, and local levels; some have close ties with the schools and others do not.

International level. Health problems are worldwide in scope, and in recent years many united efforts have been made to solve them. Outstanding work has been done by such organizations as the World Health Organization (WHO), the United Nations International Children's Emergency Fund (UNICEF), and the United Nations Educational, Scientific, and Cultural Organization (UNESCO). Committees appointed by WHO, for example, have published reports which have served as guides for school health programs throughout the world.

National level. The principal federal agencies that exert an influence on health education are the Public Health Service; the Office of Education; the Children's Bureau in the Department of Health, Education, and Welfare; and the Extension Services of the Department of Agriculture. These agencies conduct research, publish reports, suggest policies, establish standards, and offer consultation services. They work closely with state and local health units,

---

[1] See American Association for Health, Physical Education, and Recreation, *School Health Practices in the United States* (Washington, D.C.: The Association, 1961), for a representative picture of school health programs and practices in twenty-three states.

24

and some of them provide grants-in-aid that enable individual states to promote better programs.

Several types of nongovernment agencies also sponsor health projects: youth organizations, voluntary health and welfare agencies, foundations, professional societies, parent-teacher associations, labor unions, religious societies, fraternal organizations, civic clubs, life insurance companies, and industrial concerns.

National health agencies have frequently banded together to solve problems of common concern. In 1921, a number of voluntary health organizations and other agencies formed the National Health Council. The Council has established the National Health Library, has promoted the formation of state and local health councils, has encouraged youths to seek health careers, and has carried out many other projects. Cooperative ventures have also been organized to stimulate the establishment and improvement of school health programs. Excellent guidebooks have been produced by The National Conference for Cooperation in Health Education, which was established in 1940, and the Joint Committee on Health Problems in Education of the National Education Association and American Medical Association, which celebrated its golden anniversary in 1961. The biennial Conferences on Physicians and Schools, which are sponsored by the American Medical Association and are attended by leaders from the fields of medicine, public health, and education, are another example of the trend toward cooperative planning.

State level. A state develops its own health program, but it may receive various forms of assistance and incentives from federal government agencies, voluntary health organizations, professional bodies, institutions of higher learning, and private foundations. A number of cooperative school health education projects, for example, have been launched as a result of grants that state departments of education have received from the Kellogg Foundation.

All states do not organize their health programs along similar lines. The interpretation and enforcement of state health laws affecting the school child may rest with the department of health or with the department of public instruction (usually in the division of health and physical education). In some states, the two departments share the responsibilities. In such cases, final authority for health education commonly rests with the department of public instruction and matters such as sanitation, immunization, physical examinations, and clinics are in the hands of the department of health. In the past, hostility and rivalry sometimes existed between these two departments, but in most states these difficulties have been ironed out and sound cooperative working arrangements established. Today, it is not uncommon for the two departments to share personnel, appoint joint committees, and prepare joint policies and publications. In recent years, there has also been a trend toward establishing more comprehensive child health and welfare committees composed of representatives from several state departments and private agencies.

Local level. Because of the intertwining interests and responsibilities in school and community health work, the organization of programs on the local level—particularly in large cities—is quite complex. School administrators, teachers, and nonteaching employees participate in the program; city health and recreation departments assume many responsibilities; voluntary agencies, service clubs, and youth organizations make contributions; hospital associations, medical associations, churches, and other groups provide for some needs. In the early days of the health movement, most of these agencies worked independently. Consequently, there was considerable overlapping of authority, areas of conflict, competition for funds, and needless duplication of effort and facilities. Not uncommonly several agencies provided one type of service while other urgent problems were ignored. To overcome these difficulties and to coordinate the efforts of all workers, many health councils have been established in recent years on a schoolwide, systemwide, or communitywide basis. Some communities have formed councils on all three levels and have established channels of communication between them.

Three types of communitywide councils have been established: (1) those that seek solutions to local economic and social problems, some of which are related to health; (2) those that survey and provide for the overall health needs of the community; (3) those that seek solutions to particular health problems. Representatives of several health agencies, including the schools, may serve on the council. The amount and type of work that individual members do varies. They may merely exchange viewpoints and develop mutual understandings; they may agree to pool some resources and plan for interagency use of facilities; or they may plan a major attack on the health problems of the community. In such a case, they survey the existing services and problems in the community, plan overall programs to provide for local needs, and assign agencies to assume the responsibilities that they can most effectively carry out.

Responsibility for Promoting the School Health Program

The superintendent of schools is responsible for promoting the school health program and integrating it with the total educational program and the community health services. To discharge his duties, he must be thoroughly familiar with the health laws that pertain to the schools and the standards that have been proposed for the operation of sound programs. One of his responsibilities is to obtain teaching and nonteaching employees who meet the health preparatory standards recommended for their areas of work. He must solve the problem of providing adequate facilities, equipment, time, leadership, and in-service training for them. With the help of other staff members, he must also draft policies for various aspects of the health program and establish an effective public relations program. Several publications are available to guide him.[2]

Health instruction. Responsibility for the instructional program is usually assigned to a director of health and physical education, a health supervisor, or a health coordinator. All teachers are encouraged to contribute, but most of the work is done by elementary schoolteachers, homeroom teachers, or teachers in the fields of physical education, science, home economics, and health. Sometimes the school nurses are drawn into certain phases of the work. In each school building, the principal, one teacher, or a health council usually is made responsible for coordinating health instructional activities.

Health service. The health service program may be supervised by the director of health and physical education, but quite commonly a physician or nurse assumes this responsibility. In some schools, the county or city health department provides some or virtually all of the services. When this division of authority exists,

___

[2] See The National Conference on Coordination of the School Health Program, *Teamwork in School Health* (Washington, D.C.: American Association for Health, Physical Education, and Recreation, 1962). Several other important policy statements are listed in the bibliography (see items 1, 5, 15, 16, 17, 18).

school administrators work out cooperative agreements for the conduct of the program with these agencies. They also establish proper administrative relationships with organizations that supply the schools with milk, X-rays, hot lunches, preschool roundups, eyeglasses, medical equipment, or advisory services. The major responsibility of the health service staff is to establish policies and procedures for (1) health appraisals and follow-up work, (2) emergency care of the sick and injured, (3) control of communicable diseases, and (4) education of exceptional children.

The number of health service employees is determined by the size of the school district, the adequacy of its financial resources, and the public's interest in health. Sometimes a nurse may do all the work, but usually a physician and dentist are also employed. Some school districts add psychologists, visiting teachers, nutritionists, physiotherapists, dental hygienists, audiometrists, optometrists, or orthopedists to their staffs. Many schools obtain the services of some health specialists through cooperative agreements with child guidance clinics, nongovernmental agencies, or the board of health. Elementary schoolteachers and physical education and homeroom teachers also assist the health service personnel in many ways.

Healthful school living. The responsibility for promoting healthful school living rests with all staff members, but some members are assigned special duties. The superintendent strives to obtain schools, grounds, and equipment that are free from health hazards and enough custodians to maintain them properly. He outlines policies concerning the procedures that each principal, teacher, custodian, bus driver, lunchroom employee, clerk, and health staff member is to employ to promote healthful school living. Periodically, the superintendent, various members of the health staff, or representatives of the local health or fire departments inspect various aspects of the school environment: the maintenance of the buildings, grounds, and firefighting equipment, the efficiency of exit drills and civil defense measures, and the provisions for street and highway safety and school bus transportation. To protect the health of children, administrators check the length of the school day, class period, and lunch hour, and the amount of time allotted for outdoor activities and physical education. They also examine all policies regarding extracurricular and evening functions, attendance, discipline, examinations, and promotions. To protect the health of teachers, they endeavor to provide guidance for new staff members, adequate sick leave, helpful supervision, good working conditions, and reasonable work assignments.

Construction of the Curriculum

The amount of curriculum planning that takes place on the local level and the number of people who participate in it varies. In some places the staff does little more than selects textbooks and makes a token effort to comply with school health laws. Fortunately, more promising practices prevail elsewhere. In many places, curriculum construction is a continuous process that involves many people both within and outside the school. Moreover, the health program is not designed to operate as an isolated entity, but rather is integrated with many aspects of school and community life.

Work of the health council. About one-third of the schools in the United States have established health councils that bring together people who are concerned with the health of youth. Some or all of the following individuals may serve on the health council: school administrators; school health coordinators or directors of health and physical education; teachers of physical education, science, home economics, and health; members of the health service, guidance, food services, and custodial staffs; representatives of the local health department, PTA, student council, community health council, medical associations, and health and youth organizations.

Many councils were originally established on a temporary basis to solve a particular problem, but they have since become permanent bodies concerned with the total school health program. A council may (1) examine the existing program to spot gaps, overlapping activities, and other weaknesses; (2) survey the ever-changing needs of youths in the community and compile data concerning particular problems; (3) determine what school and community resources can best provide for these needs and propose a definite course of action for meeting each problem; (4) draft policies regarding various aspects of the school health program; (5) consider complaints that are received from the public and staff, provide explanations, and make corrections; (6) develop long-range plans for improving public relations and coordinating school and community health programs; and (7) appoint subcommittees to develop various aspects of the curriculum.

Exploration of the problem. The health curriculum may be constructed by one person, but more commonly a team approach is used. The team may be a subcommittee of the health council and the health teacher, health coordinator, or curriculum director usually provides the leadership. If the committee members represent varied fields of interest in the school and community, they can bring diverse viewpoints, skills, and knowledges to bear on a problem. In addition to pooling their own knowledges, the committee members usually seek assistance from other sources. They become familiar with the health laws that apply to schools and examine the state course of study (34 per cent of the states have prepared one) and those published by other states and communities. They may obtain assistance from health workshops, voluntary organizations, child research centers, government agencies, institutions of higher learning, or professional organizations.

To develop a program that will meet the needs and interests of pupils in the local community, the curriculum committee tries to discover what problems and activities are common to most pupils in each age group and the special problems that some students face. To do this they may:

1. Observe the physical, mental, social, and emotional condition of pupils;

2. Evaluate the social climate and the health and safety practices and conditions in classrooms, on the playgrounds, in the halls, and in the cafeteria;

3. Study cumulative records, health appraisals, and accident and absence reports;

4. Observe the children's home environment;

5. Hold conferences with children, parents, doctors, nurses, dentists, sanitarians, home demonstration agents, county farm agents, clergymen, and social workers;

6. Delve into data collected by public health, welfare, juvenile court, recreation, and social workers;

7. Examine census reports and county, state, and national mortality records;

8. Utilize tests or checklists to find out what pupils on various age levels know about health and safety and what their concerns, beliefs, and practices are;

9. Survey students' out-of-school activities and interests;

10. Study community health, safety, and recreation hazards, practices, and services;

11. Review research studies concerning learning, child development, and the needs and interests of youngesters;

12. Analyze citizenship responsibilities related to health;

13. Investigate vocational opportunities in health fields; and

14. Study major social trends and issues related to health.

Preparation of the program. Each school system prepares its health program somewhat differently, but many of them proceed as follows: after surveying pupils' health needs, a committee of teachers from different grade levels drafts objectives to provide for them and determines the major topics to be included in the curriculum. To insure continuity of experiences and prevent unnecessary duplication, the committee also decides what should be offered on each grade level. Every effort is made to select materials and activities that relate to the problems and interests of the given age group.

After the vertical committee has blocked out a program, horizontal committees composed of teachers of the same grade levels construct resource units to achieve the desired goals. These units provide far more resources than one teacher can use so that each instructor can select the materials from them that are particularly suitable for his pupils.

After constructing the curriculum, the committee members raise questions to evaluate their work: Has any important topic been omitted or been given insufficient emphasis? Has proper progression and continuity of learning experiences been provided for throughout the grades? Are the topics and units suitable for the age level and home backgrounds of the pupils? Has health instruction been articulated with all of the school activities, subject-matter fields, and personnel in the school and community that can make a contribution to the program? Is each topic presented at the most suitable time of year, day, and week? Do the available facilities, the size or qualifications of the staff, the local mores, or the students' home conditions render the inclusion of certain topics impractical or unrealistic? Has all unnecessary repetition been eliminated? Periodically, committees evaluate how effectively their plans have worked out, study new needs and conditions that are evolving in the society and in the community, and revise the curriculum accordingly. Sometimes this work is done in presemester or post-semester planning conferences or in summer workshops.

Placement in the Schedule

Since health is a major objective of education, the subject should be placed on a par with the more traditional courses in regard to time allotments, facilities, size of classes, credit given, and quality of teaching staff. Because health is a relatively new arrival in the curriculum and constant pressure is being exerted to introduce or expand other fields, this ideal is not always realized. Many schools, however, are making commendable progress.

Patterns of instruction. Several patterns of providing for instruction have evolved; the more common ones are incidental, correlated, integrated, and separate instruction. A school may employ one or any combination of these patterns in its master plan for health education.

Incidental instruction. All well-prepared educators engage in incidental health and safety instruction whenever a "teachable moment" arises. Mary complains about a toothache, a fire breaks out across the street, or Tom is hit by a swing. Through casual comments concerning a pupil's posture, coughing in the classroom, items on a child's cafeteria tray, and other conditions, they repeatedly focus attention on good health practices. Many desirable results accrue from this informal guidance. It helps bridge the gap that sometimes exist between knowledge and practice, and it capitalizes on moments when motivation to learn is high. Valuable as this type of teaching is, a school cannot rely upon it exclusively. Since there is no assurance that enough situations will arise spontaneously to develop the essential health knowledges, attitudes, and habits, incidental instruction must be supplemented by an organized instructional program.

Correlation.[3] Correlating health materials with other subjects and activities in the school is another popular method of instruction. School lunch periods, athletics, extracurricular activities, homeroom periods, physical examinations, and playground activities provide excellent opportunities to educate children about health and safety.

---

[3] Many suggestions for correlating health instruction on various levels can be found in books listed in the bibliography (see items 13, 15, 19, 23).

Health units and materials are often correlated with subject matter in physical education, home economics, science, social studies, and other fields. Such correlations strengthen and supplement the health program, but schools often encounter problems when they rely solely upon this type of instruction. All too frequently the same topics are correlated with several courses and other important topics are ignored. Some pupils may not receive any instruction if the health units are presented in elective courses or in courses—such as home economics—that are usually restricted to one sex. Many teachers, particularly on the secondary level, are reluctant to crowd health topics in their courses, and some of them have not had sufficient preparation in the field to do a satisfactory job.

Integration. Some or all of the education that pupils receive may be provided for through integrated units of study rather than through separate subject matter courses. This type of program, which is often referred to as "common learnings" or a "core curriculum," is organized around common human needs and problems that are closely related to the developmental levels of the pupils. Teachers plan large, unified experience units and have pupils draw upon subject matter from many fields, including health, to solve problems. Some schools devote the entire day to integrated experience units that emphasize the analyzing and solving of problems. Other schools devote a block of time to this type of unit and the rest of the day to the systematic mastery of conventional subject matter.

Health education has been integrated on the elementary level quite successfully throughout the country. When first-grade pupils pursue the theme, "How We Go To and From School and What We See on the Way," for example, many health experiences may be woven into the theme: what to wear on rainy days, how to cross the busy street, or a visit to the neighborhood dairy. Integrated or core programs have advantages: they reach all pupils and they provide opportunities for applying health knowledges to real-life problems that concern pupils. Most secondary schools, however, have retained their departmentalized curriculums, and many of those that have introduced core curriculums have not made adequate provisions for health education. Nonetheless, some progress has been made and some methods used in integrated courses for providing for the needs,

interests, and individual differences of students have spilled over into more conventional classes.

Specific courses.   Some thoughtful educators believe that incidental, correlated, and integrated instruction—alone or in combination—cannot provide an adequate junior and senior high school health education program. They advocate that junior and senior high schools organize separate health courses comparable to those offered for traditional subjects, that they require all pupils to take them, and that they select teachers who have had adequate college preparation in health.

Placement and sequence of health topics.   School administrators must not only decide how health is to be woven into the curriculum, but also on what grade levels and in what sequence various health topics are to be taught. They may adopt a continuous plan or a cycle plan or they may adopt a combination of these plans.

Continuous plan.   The continuous plan, which is the oldest and probably the most common, places continuous emphasis on major health topics: some aspects of each topic are presented each year. Advocates of this plan argue that acquiring sound health information and practices is of utmost importance and that the body of existing knowledge is vast. They believe that children must be introduced to basic health considerations as early as possible and must receive annual instruction that will reinforce and extend these learnings. This plan keeps students' attention focused on health, but it is not without its weaknesses. If teachers attempt to present all topics each year, they are apt to cover each one superficially. If no logical sequence of instruction is planned, or if textbooks of different series are used on different grade levels, some materials are apt to be repeated excessively and some important topics may be slighted.

Cycle plan.   The cycle plan, rather than emphasizing all major health topics each year, concentrates on two or three themes. Teachers single out each topic for intensive study about every two to four years; units on nutrition, for example, may be taught in Grades 2, 5, 8, and 11. This plan probably first appeared in the 1933 state course of study for elementary schools in Indiana. Oregon introduced a four-cycle plan for Grades 1–12 in 1945. Proponents of the cycle plan contend that it gives adequate emphasis to each major health problem that pupils encounter as their needs change and learning capacities expand. Moreover, it provides for progressive, cumulative learning in some depth without the duplication that frequently occurs under the continuous scheduling plan. The cycle plan is not without weaknesses. If teachers adhere to it rigidly, they may ignore current issues or pertinent situations that arise because they are not related to the topic scheduled for that time. If the plan is not carefully structured, certain topics may not be presented on the proper grade level, too much time may be assigned to some problems and too little to others, and some topics may be omitted altogether.

Combination plan.   A combination of the continuous and cycle plan is also used. Some administrators schedule health instruction that is required annually by state laws on the continuous plan and other instruction on the cycle plan. Virginia requires annual progressive consideration of each of five areas in grades one through seven. But on the secondary level, the health curriculum provides for two cycles with each of seven topics ordinarily appearing once in each cycle. Grades eight, nine, and ten comprise Cycle I and Grades eleven and twelve comprise Cycle II.

Time allotment and distribution.   The school administrator is responsible for finding adequate time for health instruction in the crowded school schedule and for distributing this time throughout the week on various grade levels. The recommended standards found in *Suggested School Health Policies*[4] can assist him in making these decisions.

Elementary level.   Health educators advocate that the time allotment for health instruction on the elementary level should at least equal that allotted to other major areas in the curriculum. Some states suggest or require that schools offer a minimum number of minutes a week. The *Elementary Course of Study* of the Commonwealth of Pennsylvania, for example, recommends short periods of instruction as the need arises in the kindergarten and Grades 1 and 2, two half-hour periods a week in Grades 3 and 4, and two forty-minute periods a week in Grades 5 and 6.

In general, two types of plans are used in scheduling health on

---

[4] National Conference for Cooperation in Health Education, Committee on School Health Policies, *Suggested School Health Policies,* 3rd ed. (Washington, D.C., and Chicago: National Education Association and American Medical Association, 1956).

the elementary level. Traditional elementary schools set aside a block of time each week for students to read health books and to discuss assigned topics, or they crowd the required hours into one semester. Many elementary schools employ more flexible schedules. Teachers plan comprehensive learning units that may include a number of health, physical, rest, and creative activities. Some units or days may be devoted exclusively to health problems while only incidental references may be made on other occasions. The teachers make periodic checks, however, to make certain that health is being given adequate emphasis.

Secondary level.   The health problems of secondary students are as varied and complex as those of elementary students: hence, they need ample time and good guidance to solve them. Administrators have devised various methods of scheduling instruction on this level. Quite commonly they combine health instruction with physical education or science courses. If combined grades and credits are given and the teacher is permitted to determine how much emphasis is to be placed on each aspect of the course, the danger always exists that health instruction may be slighted. To avoid this possibility, some administrators schedule two or three days a week for health instruction. This plan, which may be used for several or all grades in the junior and senior high school, constantly brings health to the attention of students. Teachers may find it difficult, however, to provide unified learning experiences and to sustain interest in a unit when classes meet irregularly. Moreover, the students may develop negative attitudes toward the health class if they feel that it deprives them of physical education activities, for instance. If the same person is in charge of both classes, it is important that he be fully qualified to teach health. If, as is often the case, the classes are taught in gymnasiums where the equipment and conditions are unsuitable for instruction and the classes are large, even a well-qualified teacher will find it difficult to promote effective learning.

Some schools schedule specialized health courses, such as first aid, preparation for family life, driver training, and care of the sick on a required, elective, or extracurricular basis. Unless careful overall planning is done, this type of scheduling may fail to provide pupils with a well-rounded and integrated health education. When the courses are elective, some pupils may choose not to participate in the program. When several unrelated courses are offered, the danger of duplication, omission, or overemphasis of some topics also exists.

Most authorities recommend that schools schedule required, comprehensive health courses for five days a week on the junior and senior high school levels. If funds are available, these courses can be supplemented by special health classes and extracurricular experiences. According to the Committee on School Health Policies:

> ... the minimum time allotment for the junior high school health course should be a daily period for at least two semesters during the seventh, eighth, or ninth grades. The minimum time allotment for the health course in the senior high school should be a daily period for at least two semesters, preferably during the eleventh or twelfth grades.[5]

[5] *Ibid.*, p. 12.

CHAPTER IV

Elementary Health and Safety Curriculum

Elementary teachers weld the first link between the home and school. They join parents in a cooperative effort to improve the health status, habits, and attitudes of children. Youngsters differ, of course, and teachers must provide for these differences. Planning fruitful learning experiences is easier, however, if one is familiar with the general growth patterns of pupils and with the activities that provide for common needs.

Early Elementary School Children

Children usually enter kindergarten at about the age of five and complete the third grade by the time they are nine years of age. During these years a number of changes take place.

Body development

Characteristics. They experience slow steady growth—about five pounds in weight and two inches in height a year. Their arms and legs grow longer; their bodies become more slender. Posture problems may develop. Large muscles become more developed than small ones; hand-eye coordination is difficult, but it gradually improves. Bones harden.

Needs. Children should have their height and weight checked periodically and learn how to stand, sit, and walk correctly. Their seats must be of proper size and fit. They ought to participate in vigorous outdoor games that involve the whole body. They need to learn that food, rest, activity, and freedom from disease will help them grow.

Teeth, eyes, ears

Characteristics. They lose some first teeth by six years of age and erupt some permanent teeth (four, six-year molars). Their eyes focus slowly and tire easily. They are usually farsighted; if nearsightedness develops, it appears about age eight.

Needs.   They must learn to brush their teeth regularly and properly and to visit the dentist periodically. They need to learn where new teeth will erupt and how to select foods that build sound teeth while avoiding those that cause decay. They should be given screening tests to detect any vision, hearing, and speech problems. They need to acquire information about sense organs: they must learn to sit where they can see and hear adequately and to refrain from rubbing their eyes, biting hard objects, and putting foreign objects into their eyes, ears, and mouths.

Nutrition, digestion, elimination

Characteristics.   Their appetites are usually good except at breakfast, but they have strong likes and dislikes, are suspicious of new foods, may neglect vegetables, and may bolt food. They usually have bowel movements once or twice a day.

Needs.   They require motivation that encourages them to eat a good breakfast and a variety of foods. They must learn how diet affects the way they feel and grow, what foods aid growth, and what foods to avoid between meals. They must also learn to wash before eating, to select healthful foods, to eat slowly, and to use good table manners.

Activity, sleep, rest, relaxation

Characteristics.   They possess abundant energy and are eager to play, construct, and participate. They tire easily and have a short attention span. Their interests and emotional reactions shift rapidly.

Needs.   These youngsters need to understand the importance of getting enough rest and sleep (eleven to twelve hours); five- and six-year-olds may require afternoon naps. Their activities should be varied and of short duration; they ought to have considerable freedom of movement and frequent rest periods.

Illness and accidents

Characteristics.   Communicable diseases, colds, gastrointestinal upsets, and ear infections are common, but become progressively less marked through this age span. Eye injuries, falls, drowning, and automobile and bicycle accidents are common.

Needs.   They must acquire immunization protection and knowledge of its value and learn to regard the nurse, doctor, and dentist as helpful friends and to obtain prompt care when ill or injured. They must learn to control coughing and sneezing and to understand the importance of wearing suitable clothing for various types of weather and activities. They must learn how to avoid accidents and what to do when one occurs. They require continuous observation for signs of illness or departure from normal behavior, periodic physical examinations, and prompt correction of problems. They must be provided with adequate safeguards in school—supervision and facilities—to protect them from injuries.

Personal care

Characteristics.   They gradually improve in their ability to care for their physical needs—bathing, dressing, and combing hair—but are apt to dawdle and do a sketchy job.

Needs.   They should become more familiar with the social and health reasons for cleanliness and good grooming and become increasingly self-reliant about personal care.

Intellectual, emotional, social development

Characteristics.   Early elementary school children possess some reasoning ability, but lack experience on which to base judgments. Their mastery of language improves. They have some concept of time and distance, but for most part are interested in the here and now.

Their judgment is influenced by strong likes and dislikes. They become upset easily, but move quickly from tears to laughter. The adjustment to school life may cause physical and emotional stress.

They are more self-centered than group-oriented; they crave adult attention, approval, and affection, and are strongly attached to their mothers and teachers and want considerable help from them. They gradually grow in independence, exhibit greater interest in group activities, and become more sensitive to opinion of peers and less concerned with those of adults.

Young children love babies and play with both sexes, but by age eight they become aware of individual and sex differences and want some specific information.

They are highly dramatic, imaginative, curious, active, and imitative; they love fairy tales, comic books, television, and rhythms.

Needs.   They must be given health explanations that are simple and nontechnical. They ought to experience dramatic play, rhythms, and active games that are not too complicated.

They should be oriented to the school building and routines and to neighborhood friends—policemen, storekeepers, and the like. They must learn to work and play alone and with others: to share work, ideas, possessions; to compete honestly; to observe safety rules; to take turns; to assume responsibility; to help establish rules and standards and abide by them. They must learn to face reality; to understand that they cannot always win and that tears do not solve problems. They should be given opportunities to make friends, to express themselves in various ways, to show their best effort, to experience some success, to receive praise. They need to receive answers to their sex questions, preferably from their parents.

Early Elementary Health and Safety Curriculum

No one curriculum will meet the needs of all the children in every community, but there is general agreement that teachers on *all* levels should give due consideration to the following broad topics: (1) personal cleanliness and appearance; (2) growth, nutrition, and elimination (including, on the upper levels, the problems of tobacco, alcohol, and drugs); (3) activity, rest, relaxation, and sleep; (4) prevention and control of disease; (5) safety and first aid; (6) dental and medical attention; (7) body structure and function; (8) mental and emotional health; (9) family living (including sex education); and (10) community health. Because it is not practicable to outline all of the curricular materials that pertain to each topic on each school level, this chapter and the one that follows will merely suggest appropriate activities for a few of these topics on each level.

Elementary school teachers, as well as teachers on all other levels, assume some responsibility for integrating their instruction with the activities of the health service staff. When immunization programs, tuberculin tests, physical and dental examinations, weighing and measuring programs, or screening tests are conducted in the school, elementary school teachers enlist the active cooperation of parents and pupils before, during, and after the event. In classes, letters, and conferences, they explain the value of these measures, encourage participation, dispel fears, and enliven interest by describing the procedures that will be used. Afterwards, they help interpret the findings and encourage parents to take corrective measures.

Each day elementary school teachers informally observe pupils, note conditions that deviate from normal, and send suspicious cases to the nurse or principal. They check for skin and scalp eruptions, red and crusted eyelids, earaches or discharge from the ear, excessive coughing and nasal discharge, unusual pallor, fever, sore throat, swollen glands, nausea, headaches, frequent trips to the toilet, lack of appetite, excessive fatigue, emotional upsets, excessive aggressiveness or withdrawal, and symptoms of communicable diseases.

Getting acquainted. Leaving a familiar home to enter the strange, exciting world of the school is a big event in the lives of children. Because some things puzzle and worry them, they need learning experiences that will enable them to take this transition in stride. A teacher can help by providing orientation activities such as those suggested below:

1. Use a chart and pictures to illustrate daily routines; make up a story about what the bell "tells" us; develop skits concerning tardiness. Show where clothes are to be put and the correct procedures for putting them there. Have pupils establish rules for getting and putting away supplies and have them observe safety precautions when using them. Encourage pupils to volunteer to obtain milk, feed pets, and check cleanliness of the room or grounds.

2. Discuss the importance of handwashing before eating. Cut out pictures of foods for lunch and mid-morning snacks that help children grow. Discuss safe and healthful behavior in halls, on stairways, at drinking fountains, and in the lavatories. Take the children on a tour of the building to practice what has been learned. Have them meet the cafeteria employees and learn how to obtain food, where to sit, and how to carry a tray. Show them what table manners and clean-up procedures to observe so that the lunch period will be a more pleasant and healthful experience.

3. Discuss and practice fire drill routines. Take children to visit a nearby fire station.

4. Tour the gymnasium and playground and have the physical educator explain where pupils are permitted to play, the safe way to use various equipment, what to do when hurt, and where to put trash.

5. Take the children to visit the principal, nurse, custodian, and school clerk, who will explain and exhibit things that they do to help children.

Getting to and from school. Many problems that early elementary children must solve are concerned with getting to and from school. The teacher can help them by doing the following:

1. Have them learn their names, addresses, and telephone numbers. Have a policeman discuss the importance of going straight home from school and the danger of accepting rides from strangers.

2. Have them dramatize desirable and undesirable practices to observe while awaiting, boarding, riding, and leaving a bus, or walking to and from school during different seasons. Discuss why walking is good for pupils and dictate stories about the beautiful, interesting, and funny things one sees on the way to school.

3. Have a policeman or member of the school patrol discuss safety practices for pedestrians to observe. Take a safety walk to a corner with traffic lights. Make portable traffic lights and dramatize methods of crossing the street; have pupils take the roles of drivers, policemen, and pedestrians. Draw a map with streets and traffic lights; have pupils mark where they live and help them select the safest route home.

4. Plan a good breakfast. Visit a grocery store to examine a variety of breakfast fruits, cereals, and milk drinks and see how food is kept fresh and clean.

5. Discuss social and health reasons for washing, brushing teeth, cleaning nails, combing hair, and having clean clothes and handkerchiefs. Have pupils demonstrate proper way to do these things. Periodically check their practices. Cut out pictures of proper clothing to use for different activities and seasons and discuss health reasons for each choice.

Care of teeth. When pupils lose their first teeth, they are curious about the experience and interested in learning about teeth. Since a large majority of them probably have cavities, dental education is needed. The teacher may do the following:

1. Use a model to show the proper method of brushing teeth and hold toothbrush drills.

2. Using songs, stories, charts, and pictures, get pupils to discuss when to clean teeth, where new teeth will erupt, how teeth help us chew food and affect our appearance and speech, how tooth cleanliness makes one look and feel and how it may prevent decay, why teeth decay and how tooth decay affects our health, and how to protect teeth at play, at drinking fountains, and on the bus.

3. Visit a nearby dentist or invite him to class. Have him exhibit his tools and explain how he uses them to help children. Have him tell them how to care for their teeth. Read stories about visits to the dentist that can be obtained from the American Dental Association.

4. Mimeograph a chart and permit children to color in a square each time they brush their teeth. Exhibit charts.

5. Have the children build a "make-believe" dental office and play patient and dentist. Make a magazine for the office that includes original stories, pictures of food that build sound teeth and those that cause decay, and drawings of healthy and decayed teeth. Arrange an exhibit of teeth or models of them.

Intermediate School Children

Most children in Grades 4, 5, and 6 are nine, ten, and eleven years of age, respectively. They are sometimes referred to as "pre-adolescents."

Body development

Characteristics.   Slow steady gains in height and weight are typical, but some pupils—particularly girls—experience a growth spurt at end of period. Some girls begin to menstruate and modesty becomes important to them.

Eye-hand coordination is good; speed, accuracy, rhythmic sense, and motor skills improve. Muscular strength lags behind physical growth; some pupils begin to slouch. Boys, particularly, want to build strong bodies and develop their muscles. Youngsters become curious about their bodies and minds and how they work.

Needs.   They must learn about the body's organs and processes: how they function, how they work together, and what health practices will make them function properly. They should become aware of the relationship between health habits and motor skills and physical development. They need vigorous physical exercise, instruction in body mechanics, and self-testing activities that will enable them to appraise their abilities.

Maturer students need a clear concept of human reproduction, menstruation, and seminal emissions.

Teeth, eyes, ears

Characteristics.   Permanent teeth continue to erupt. Normal farsightedness of earlier period disappears and students can do more close work; however, nearsightedness may develop.

Needs.   Examinations may reveal need for orthodontia, care of caries, and eyeglasses. Students should learn that crooked teeth can be straightened, that sound teeth add to physical attractiveness, and that decayed teeth affect general health. They need to acquire an elementary understanding of the structure and function of the eyes, ears, and teeth. They must develop a respect for the special senses and a desire to care for them properly.

Nutrition, digestion, elimination

Characteristics.   They have good appetites and will eat a wider variety of food. They have good control of elimination.

Needs.   They need to acquire an understanding of how food helps one maintain health and achieve success in work and play. They must understand the need for and function of proteins, minerals, vitamins, fats, and carbohydrates. They should learn that coffee, tea, tobacco, and alcoholic beverages are not healthful for growing children. They ought to obtain an elementary understanding of the digestive processes and establish practices that aid digestion. They need to learn how wastes are eliminated from the body and what foods help one get rid of waste.

Activity, sleep, rest, relaxation

Characteristics.   Intermediate school children sleep well and have a high energy level which may lead them to "overdo." Boys, particularly, love vigorous activities and dangerous challenges. Children of this age exhibit interest in a wide range of play activities. With the approach of adolescence, they may become rather inactive.

Needs.   They need ten to twelve hours of sleep and ought to avoid excitable activities before bedtime and meals. They should receive instruction in team games, crafts, dance and sport skills, and carefully controlled competitive activities in which emphasis is placed on safety measures. They need to explore the relationship between rest and success in sports, school work, and relations with others. They should learn how exercise and recreation ease tensions, establish the practice of resting before becoming too fatigued, and develop interests and practices that provide relaxation.

Illness and accidents

Characteristics.   They experience fewer respiratory infections, contagious diseases, gastrointestinal upsets, and earaches. Their interest in health habits diminishes; much backsliding occurs. During this adventurous age, accidents increase—particularly those involving bicycles, burns, and automobiles.

Needs.   They must continue to receive periodic health examinations and acquire safety skills and knowledges relating to water, woods, and game activities. They must be supervised when at play. They need to study accidents and diseases that are typical of the age group and learn how to avoid them. They must learn about personal and community practices that affect their health and assume responsibilities in fire drills, in safety campaigns, or as members of the school patrol. They should learn something about the nature of bacteria and the conditions that encourage and discourage their growth. Children of this age ought to learn to administer first aid treatment for cuts, bites, and nosebleeds.

Personal care

Characteristics.   Intermediate school girls are interested in their appearance. Most pupils know how to observe good personal hygiene practices, but backsliding is common. Postural habits vary.

Needs.   They require guidance concerning grooming and opportunities to explore the relationship between health habits, appearance (including sitting and standing posture), and social success. They should learn about the structure and function of the skin and the elimination of wastes through the skin. They need to become acquainted with the relationship between bacteria and cleanliness and the prevention and control of disease.

Intellectual, emotional, social development

Characteristics.   They become more dependable, responsible, and capable of self-direction. Considerable intellectual development takes place and their attention span increases. They engage in many varied activities and are extremely eager to experiment and to learn about new things.

Their absorption with fantasy declines, and they become keenly interested in the community, the nation, other lands, ancient times, and outer space. Their concept of time and space relationships improves.

They tend to resent adult domination, nagging, and displays of excessive anxiety or affection. They are apt to be over-critical of parents and teacher, but may worship a favorite adult. They like to participate in decision-making, but usually respect fairly administered adult authority.

They crave recognition, particularly from peers. Their strong sense of rivalry impels them to seek status through superior physical, social, or intellectual performance, but they are quite critical of themselves and easily discouraged. They frequently engage in silly, boisterous behavior in order to gain attention.

Gang loyalty is highly developed; gang fights occur frequently. Clubs continually spring up, shift members, and then, because of diverging interests, collapse. Dressing and acting like friends is extremely important.

Boys scorn girls and exclude them from their games, but reveal their underlying interest by chasing and teasing them. Boys enjoy activities with men and often consider women fussy or bossy. Girls disdain the opposite sex until the end of this age period, when they may express an interest in a particular boy.

Needs.   Children of this age must receive guidance in judging how many activities to undertake. They need to study the scientific reasons underlying bodily processes and health practices, explore the "why" and "how" as well as the "what." They should learn that all people face fears, jealousies, frustrations, limitations, and defects and must make adjustments to them in an acceptable manner. Their expanding interests and love of hero worship may be satisfied by studying community and national health problems and health leaders of the past and present.

They must be allowed to establish themselves with age mates through clubs, committee work, competitive team games, and wholesome coeducational activities in which the need for cooperation, safety, and fair play is stressed. They should be given opportunities to establish their own standards, criticize their own behavior, make their own decisions, and carry out their own plans under tactful teacher guidance. They can experience some recognition and success by setting up attainable group and personal health goals, planning how to achieve them, executing their plans, and evaluating their progress.

Intermediate Health and Safety Curriculum

Intermediate pupils need learning experiences that will widen their horizons and reinforce the attitudes, understandings, and practices that they acquired in the first three grades. Health units become more comprehensive on this level, for students can probe problems in greater depth. Proper attention is given to the ten major health areas (see p. 41), but some of them may receive special emphasis.

Body growth, structure, and operation.   Children at this age are extremely curious about why and how things happen. They are interested in their eyes, hearts, stomachs, blood, and feet. They want to know what their body looks like inside. Thus, this is an ideal time to acquaint youngsters with the structure and function of their body organs and systems and help them develop a wholesome appreciation of their bodies.

Body organs and processes.   Use a model or wall chart to illustrate body organs and systems. Make a paper frame of the body and have pupils cut out and insert organs as they study them. Discuss, dramatize, and illustrate the function of each organ and system, how they work together, and the health practices that help them function properly. Use bellows to demonstrate breathing. Check the rate of respiration when studying, sleeping, and exercising and discuss why it differs. Obtain a chest X-ray and study the size and position of the lungs, bronchial tubes, and heart. Have the children listen to the heart beat with a stethoscope and take pulse pressure before and after exercise. Discuss why it differs and the need for rest during play.

Bones and muscles.   Have youngsters feel their own bones and joints to see how they work. Examine a skeleton or chart of bones and muscles. Attach elastic to skeletal arm bones to show working of antagonistic muscles. Make a model of arm bones and muscles with wood, hinges, rubber strips, and string to show how muscles contract. Obtain animal bones: note cartilage, joints, various layers in a cross-section of a bone. If a pupil breaks a bone, have the class examine an X-ray and discuss the repair of tissue, the need to develop muscles that have not been used for some time, and the kinds of foods that build bones. Have a football player or soldier discuss the physical conditioning program they receive. Compare pictures of athletes and undernourished, unmuscular figures; note the differences and discuss the causes.

Growth and development.   Have the children observe different types of cells in a microscope and study enlarged diagrams of them. Have them observe a cut or burn as it heals and discuss repair of tissue. Show that food, water, and sunlight are needed for growth by depriving similar plants of different essentials and supplying one plant with all requirements. Conduct animal feeding experiments.

Senses.   Examine a large model or diagram of the eye, nose, ear, and skin. Have the children report on persons with sense impairment—Helen Keller, Thomas Edison. Take the children to visit a class for the deaf or blind. Blindfold students and have them identify objects by taste, feel, odor, and sound. Use eye charts, tuning forks, audiometers, and objects of various textures and densities so that pupils can note range of sense discrimination, detect personal sense problems, and plan protective and corrective measures.

Family life.   Children should understand the importance and necessity of family life, the unique roles played by various members of the family, and the need for teamwork and tolerance in the home.

1. Have pupils discuss a family holiday or vacation: Where did they go and why? What did each member of the family do to help in preparing for the trip, on the way, when they got there? What safety precautions did they observe (for swimming, sunburn, poison ivy)? What made the trip fun?

2. Have the children plan a family party: sending out the invitations, planning the entertainment, making introductions, preparing and serving a simple lunch, and cleaning up afterward.

3. List ways in which the health of various members of the family affect happiness in the home. Dramatize the contributions that father, mother, brothers, sisters, and grandparents make to the group. Divide the class into committees and have them list ways to make home life more pleasant after school, before school, in the evening, at mealtime, and on weekends. Compile a master list and have pupils appraise their efforts periodically. Conduct home surveys to discover what safety precautions have been taken to protect various members of the family and what needs to be done.

4. To help youngsters make a wholesome sex adjustment use the National Education Association–American Medical Association booklet, *A Story About You,* which tells how life begins, how people grow, and the advances that are made during adolescence. Have the girls view the movie, *The Story of Menstruation* which can be obtained free from International Cellucotton Products Co., Chicago, Illinois. Examine "It's Normal, It's

Natural, It has a Purpose" and the teacher's guide on menstruation, "From Fiction to Facts." These booklets, which are distributed free by Tampax Inc., contain excellent teaching suggestions.

Community life.   Children need to learn how the community protects their health and how they can contribute to community welfare.

1. Have pupils study health services that are rendered by various community agencies and citizens. Take children to visit them or obtain speakers to come to class to discuss their work. Have the children participate in community improvement projects: litter control, rabies control, or immunization program.

2. Conduct health, safety, or recreation surveys in the school or community. Have pupils determine what items to check, report their findings, and discuss what can be done to improve existing situations. Have pupils undertake a specific improvement project.

3. Have committees investigate the health standards and safety precautions that businessmen must or do observe in dairies, eating establishments, farms, factories, beauty parlors, bakeries, swimming pools, theaters, and construction projects.

4. Have the children analyze an accident or catastrophe—fire, drowning, automobile accident, tornado—that was of local or historical significance. Why did it occur? Could anything have been done to prevent it? What types of service did various agencies render? What did people do when the incident occurred and what should they have done?

5. Have the children read stories and see movies about men who have contributed to health—Pasteur, Jenner, Leeuwenhoek, Salk. (The booklet *16 American Health Heroes* can be obtained free from the Metropolitan Life Insurance Company.)

6. Show the children how to use a magnifying glass to observe mold on bread or fruit, and a microscope to observe germs. Select two apples; peel one and place it in a dark warm place; expose the other one to air and sunlight; note the result in a few days. Have the children make posters to show various ways in which disease is carried and different methods of preventing its spread. Have pupils draw up a code of behavior to observe when they have colds.

CHAPTER V

Junior and Senior High School
Health and Safety Curriculum

When students enter junior high school, they begin to bid farewell to childhood and to take their first faltering steps toward adulthood. Guiding them through these exciting and turbulent years is a challenging task. This duty is easier to discharge if one possesses some knowledge of the growth patterns and needs of adolescents.

Junior High School Children

Most children in Grades 7, 8, and 9 are twelve, thirteen, and fourteen years of age, respectively. One can expect them to exhibit certain characteristics and needs.

Body development

Characteristics.   Rapid physical growth takes place with a disproportionate growth in the extremities. The hands, feet, and nose may appear oversized. Strength increases as muscular and skeletal systems develop, but the heart and circulatory systems do not always keep abreast of other developments. Awkwardness, poor coordination, fatigue, and poor posture are commonplace. Wide variations in growth patterns exist among pupils and between sexes. Girls are often taller and heavier than boys.

Reproductive organs are maturing rapidly: girls menstruate and their hips and breasts develop; boys experience change of voice and growth of hair on face. Girls mature one or two years earlier than boys. Biological changes cause some worry and embarrassment, particularly for pupils who mature earlier or later than their age mates.

Needs.   Children should learn that variations in growth patterns and sexual maturity are normal. They need to acquire accurate information about body structure and function, adolescent growth

51

processes, sexual development, and individual differences. It is essential that they learn to accept their physiques, the changes that are taking place in their bodies, and their masculine or feminine roles in society.

Pupils ought to learn how tobacco affects the body and why it is best to refrain from smoking. They should recognize that a relationship exists between emotions and health. They require periodic physical examinations and guidance to help them correct remedial weaknesses. They need sympathetic guidance concerning posture problems. At this age, youngsters should acquire some proficiency in vigorous physical activities that are modified (as to time, distance, speed, pressure to win) in accordance with their strength and endurance.

Teeth, eyes, ears

Characteristics.   Permanent dentition, except for wisdom teeth, is completed by the time children are fourteen. Youngsters are concerned about straightening their teeth. Vision and hearing defects increase.

Needs.   Youngsters ought to have regular examinations and to have their defects corrected. They should learn what orthodontia does for health and appearance and receive guidance about accepting the discomfort and embarrassment of orthodontia. Pupils must learn the causes and symptoms of eyestrain and hearing problems and ways of avoiding them. They should investigate the relationship between eye-strain and health, posture, schoolwork, and appearance, and learn to wear glasses if needed.

Nutrition, digestion, elimination

Characteristics.   Children at this age possess ravenous appetites and are apt to satisfy their hunger between meals with candies, hot dogs, and soft drinks. Some diet to increase or decrease weight. Constipation is common because of faulty eating habits, irregular regimen, and emotional problems.

Needs.   Students must learn to select substantial, well-balanced meals and to buy nourishing lunches and drinks. They should acquire an understanding of caloric requirements and the ability to identify foods that are rich sources of carbohydrates, fats, proteins, and the different vitamins and minerals. It is essential that they appreciate the dangers of unsupervised dieting and understand the relationship between nutrition and fatigue, illness, and growth. They need to learn the causes of malnutrition and common deficiency diseases and how to prevent them, and they should learn the causes of constipation and the natural methods of correcting it.

Activity, rest, sleep, relaxation

Characteristics. Youngsters of this age are active, want to stay up late, may initiate too many activities, and may pursue them beyond the point of fatigue. They tire easily and sometimes appear lazy, sluggish, and irritable. Most of them exhibit a keen interest in competitive activities and team sports.

Needs. These pupils require nine to eleven hours of sleep and should assume responsibility for establishing a well-balanced program of work, rest, and recreation. They need to perceive that rest helps them resist disease and improves their personal appearance and efficiency at work. They should develop sufficient skill to experience some success in wholesome recreational and competitive sport activities.

Illness and accidents

Characteristics. Junior high school children are relatively free from communicable diseases and experience fewer acute illnesses but more brief ones. The accident rate reaches the peak at this age, and many accidents occur in school. Youngsters may be overanxious about their health.

Needs. They must understand the principal causes of accidents and fires and observe sound safety practices at home, in recreational activities, in school, and on bicycles. They should acquire some skill in first aid and home nursing procedures and assume responsibility for preventing and caring for minor injuries and illnesses. It is important for them to obtain knowledge about tuberculosis, tuberculin tests, and X-rays. They must be made to realize that it is best to consult a competent doctor and to refrain from self-medication. In this relation, they may investigate primitive beliefs, present superstitions, and recent discoveries concerning health and disease. Students should become acquainted with health and safety agencies from the local to the international levels and contribute services to some of them.

Personal care

Characteristics. Youngsters at this age are deeply concerned about their appearance and with such problems as acne and excessive perspiration, which detract from their physical attractiveness.

Needs. Students should accept the reality of their appearance and make it as pleasing as possible. They can do this by learning to select and care for clothing and shoes, how to use cosmetics, and how to care for skin, nails, and hair. They also ought to learn the causes, preventive measures, and cures for cold sores, blackheads, boils, dandruff, athlete's foot, halitosis, and perspiration.

Intellectual, emotional, social

Characteristics. Their mental growth is not as accelerated as their physical growth. Their ability to plan and to accumulate facts improves more rapidly than their ability to organize and interpret information and to execute plans.

Moral and religious values are of concern to them. They are more willing to postpone satisfactions and work toward distant goals.

The social and biological process of becoming an adult and the strange surroundings of the junior high school may cause emotional problems. Pupils worry about their appearance and popularity. Their moods are unpredictable, and they shift from demands for independence to a longing for adult direction and reassurance: one day they are self-assured, overly aggressive, or disrespectful; the next they are shy, sensitive, fearful, or withdrawn; one day they are well-groomed, industrious, and cooperative; the next they are sloppy, lazy, and unreliable. Their self-confidence is easily shaken. If things go wrong they are apt to blame others, withdraw, or resort to fantasies.

The desire for privacy and the longing to be free of adult restrictions becomes quite intense. They may become ashamed of their parents or intolerant of younger sisters and brothers. Arguments with parents and teachers about their behavior and rights are common.

Some youths develop a rebellious, know-it-all attitude and seek exciting adult experiences before they are ready for them; many of them experiment with smoking and assume affectations of dress, speech, and handwriting.

They are interested in members of the opposite sex, but are apt to become embarrassed, speechless, or silly in their presence. "Crushes" on singers, athletes, or movie stars are common.

Many youngsters are anxious to earn money and may obtain part-time jobs. They begin to think of selecting a vocation, but often focus their attention on the more glamorous and adventurous jobs.

The desire for personal recognition and group acceptance is strong. Age-mate codes are more important to them than the approval of adults. Youngsters move from group to group until they establish social acceptance. Cliques may be quite cruel in their exclusion of others, and the rejected youngsters may feel lonely and insecure and may withdraw or become rebellious.

Needs. Children of this age must have ample opportunities to read and explore, to evaluate and order their findings, and to make practical applications of them. They should participate in orientation activities that ease their adjustment to the seventh grade.

They need to associate with patient, understanding, good-humored adults who will help them establish their objectives and evaluate their progress, status, and abilities; make a wise choice of activities and friends; make prudent use of time and money; build a set of values for themselves and develop the courage and self-discipline to follow those convictions; and develop a favorable, wholesome, and realistic concept of themselves.

Students must have opportunities to plan and carry out projects and to learn that freedom carries responsibilities. They should participate in activities that make them appreciate and take pride in the family and contribute to family happiness and welfare. Youngsters need experience in clubs, teams, committees, and social groups to achieve group acceptance and receive some recognition. They must learn how to be at ease and well-mannered in social situations. It is important that they recognize the traits of well-adjusted and well-liked people, appraise their own personalities, and endeavor to establish practices that will enable them to get along with others.

Junior High School
Health and Safety Curriculum

When youngsters move from the homelike, self-contained, elementary classroom to a big, busy, unfamiliar junior high school, they worry about making friends and adjusting to routines. They are extremely conscious of their appearance and the bodily changes they are experiencing. When planning learning experiences for them, the teacher must keep these factors in mind.

Health appraisals. Because junior high school students are extremely curious and concerned about themselves, it is easy to arouse interest in instruction by having them appraise their health status and habits. If this is done about the time that they receive health examinations, each activity will reinforce the learnings in the other, and both activities will be more meaningful. In this type of unit one might provide the following experiences.

1. Have pupils fill out health status and practices appraisal forms. The teacher may provide them or the pupils may construct them. Have them study the findings, spot the practices and defects that ought to be corrected, outline plans for doing this, estimate the amount of time that the changes will require, and periodically evaluate their progress.

2. Have the school nurse explain the value of periodic health examinations, the importance of items on medical record forms, what takes place during an examination, and what one can expect to learn. Have pupils or outside speakers discuss why health examinations are given to school children, athletes, soldiers, and people who apply for insurance and employment.

3. Discuss the types of tests that physicians make and why, and have some of them demonstrated. Arrange for an exhibition of pictures or actual items that doctors and dentists use to appraise health status.

4. Have pupils find out what people in the school and community will help them appraise and solve their physical, emotional, and social problems. Have them investigate how and where they can obtain these services. View movies of the preparatory training and work of people in the health professions.

Growing up. Pupils are often worried or embarrassed about their growth patterns, and they appreciate learning experiences that guide them through this period of adjustment.

1. Provide a box in which they can drop questions about problems that bother them. (Why am I so fat? Will I always be bigger or smaller than members of the opposite sex?) Use the questions as a basis for discussion.

2. Have pupils brings snapshots to show their development since babyhood. Discuss the changes that take place in the body, abilities, interests, responsibilities, and freedom at various ages.

3. Investigate the effect of heredity, diet, endocrine glands, exercise, and health habits on growth, appearance, and behavior.

4. Show movies or provide pamphlets and books concerning adolescent physical changes.

Safety.   Because junior high school pupils have many accidents, the Red Cross Junior First Aid course is often offered on this level. Since the bicycle is a common mode of transportation for pupils, learning experiences relating to its use are also appropriate.

1. Have pupils plan and present an assembly program in which they depict the right and wrong ways to select, maintain, and operate bicycles and explain the school regulations regarding them.

2. Have pupils prepare a self-evaluation checklist of safe bicycle practices.

3. Invite a policeman to discuss the causes and control of accidents and the licensing and inspection of bicycles.

4. Organize school bicycle patrols, clubs, courts, and trips through which pupils can promote safer operation of bicycles.

5. Keep a record of local bicycle accidents—sex of rider, time of day, cause of accident, weather conditions, condition of vehicle, and violation of law involved. Plot location of accident on a map. Analyze the findings.

6. Take bicycle performance tests that can be obtained from the National Safety Council, Chicago, Illinois, and the Center for Safety Education, New York University.

Getting along with others.   Junior high school pupils need learning experiences that will help them get along with others.

1. Have pupils, parents, and specialists discuss desirable and undesirable ways of coping with problems that arise in relations with parents, siblings, teachers, and boy- and girlfriends. Create sociodramas or draw cartoons and posters to illustrate specific situations such as the use of the telephone.

2. Have pupils fill out a readymade personality rating scale or one that they compile themselves. Have them evaluate the findings, make definite plans to improve, and periodically report on their progress.

3. Have a psychologist discuss the characteristics of emotionally healthy and unhealthy people and methods of protecting and improving mental health.

4. Show movies and collect a classroom library on subjects relating to dating, grooming, growing up, and etiquette.

5. Have pupils choose and plan a school party, learn how to make introductions, draft a code of behavior, and assume responsibility for the event.

6. Study the structure and function of the nervous system and endocrine glands and their relationship to growth, health, and behavior. Investigate the damaging effect of worry and tension and methods of avoiding it.

Personal appearance.   Pupils who are seeking social acceptance and are adjusting to growth changes become deeply concerned about their appearance and appreciate tactful guidance.

1. Discuss the relationships among good posture, healthy skin, hair, teeth, eyes, nails and such factors as diet, exercise, rest, general health status, social acceptance, economic success, and self-confidence.

2. Invite a personnel director to discuss personal appearance in relation to job opportunities and advancement. Read stories about the care that actors, athletes, military men, and successful career people give to their appearance and physical fitness.

3. Discuss causes and signs of poor posture, eyestrain, foot problems, dental problems, acne, blackheads, perspiration, athlete's foot, impetigo, ringworm, pediculosis, sunburn, and chapping. Demonstrate some preventive and control measures. Evaluate personal practices.

4. Have the pupils and home economics teacher discuss and demonstrate how to select clothing, shoes, and accessories, and how to care for them. Arrange a style show to exhibit appropriate apparel and make-up for different occasions, figures, activities, and seasons.

5. Take candid camera shots of pupils and use plumb line and mirror observation to analyze standing and sitting posture. Analyze the effect that various posture poses have on respiration, digestion, appearance, and fatigue. Discuss the relationship between posture and feet. Examine models of the foot structure and determine how it works. Determine whether the arch is "weak" by wetting the sole of the foot and making an impression on paper.

6. Have a dentist explain and demonstrate through pictures what orthodontia can do in terms of health, appearance, and digestion. Discuss the problems and value of learning to live with braces.

7. Draw a cross section of the skin; label the parts and explain the function of each. Have a nurse or skin specialist explain why adolescents have skin problems and how to care for the skin. Create sociodramas that explore problems relating to bathing, perspiration, halitosis, and the use of perfume. Have girls investigate the opinions of parents, employers, and boys concerning make-up for teenage girls. Discuss products and practices that harm the skin, hair, eyes, and teeth and collect newspaper clippings of specific incidents. Evaluate advertisements for soaps, creams, suntan oils, deodorants, shampoos, and dentifrices.

8. Have a specialist discuss proper methods of caring for the hair and fingernails and of applying make-up. Compile a list of sanitary practices to check when selecting a barber or beauty shop.

Senior High School Children

Most children in Grades 10, 11, and 12 are fifteen to eighteen years of age, respectively. One can expect them to have certain basic characteristics and needs.

Body development

Characteristics. Growth usually slows down by the age of sixteen, but great differences exist between early and late maturers. Feet, hands, and features are in better proportion to the rest of the body; a more balanced physiological condition is reached; the development of the heart begins to catch up with that of other organs. Endurance, coordination, dexterity, and posture improve. These are the years of peak physical performance.

Some boys do not reach puberty until this period; in general, secondary sex characteristics become more pronounced.

Needs. Pupils should assume more responsibility themselves for obtaining regular health checkups, appraising their health needs, and correcting defects. They ought to deepen and broaden their understanding of normal and abnormal body structure and function, and learn to maintain proper sitting and standing posture. They need regular exercise and should strive for proficiency in some physical activities that are suitable for their strength and maturity. They should also become familiar with discoveries that doctors and scientists have made to help maintain the normal functioning of the body.

Teeth, eyes, ears

Characteristics. Except for wisdom molars, all permanent teeth are present. Eye and ear defects continue to increase.

Needs. Pupils must assume greater responsibility for self-direction in regard to care and corrective measures. They ought to become familiar with new discoveries and community efforts that will improve the care of the eyes, teeth, and ears and that will aid the blind and deaf. They must realize the importance of budgeting for health care in future family life, and learn to evaluate advertisements for health products.

Nutrition, digestion, elimination

Characteristics. Food excesses, fads, "picky" appetites are common. Girls may experiment with reducing diets and weight control aids. Use of cathartics is common.

Needs. Pupils continue to require a high caloric diet. They need to review desirable nutritional standards and practice selecting food accordingly. They should study recent findings concerning the relationship between diet and weight control, physical fitness, and diseases of adulthood. They must also learn to select sanitary places in which to eat, how to provide for proper preservation of food, and how to observe hygienic practices when preparing, serving, or eating food. They need to learn how to get their money's worth when buying food, how to prepare low-cost, nutritious diets, and how to evaluate advertisements for food products, diet aids, and cures for indigestion and constipation.

Activity, rest, sleep, relaxation

Characteristics. Students continue to engage in skilled sports, but of a more limited variety. Girls become less interested in vigorous athletics, but enjoy sports and dance activities that help them become popular with the opposite sex. Many students who lack physical skills withdraw from participation and become spectators or seek thrills through commercial amusements.

Needs. Students of this age require eight to ten hours of sleep. They should acquire skill in constructive recreational pursuits, particularly those that will provide them with exercise, outdoor experiences, and relaxation in adult life. They must recognize the relationship between family recreational experiences and health and happiness, and become familiar with wholesome, inexpensive types of family recreation that are available in the local community. They must also recognize the importance of making provisions for varied and wholesome recreation in the community.

It is also important that they learn to appraise the amount of time they can devote to part-time employment, social activities, and study in view of their need for rest and their desire to achieve lifetime goals.

Illness and accidents

Characteristics. Youths are eager to drive automobiles and many become involved in accidents. Accidents lead as a cause of death; cancer is a major cause of death from disease; venereal disease presents a problem. Students exhibit a greater interest in disease control and prevention.

Needs. Students must learn to recognize symptoms of illness, seek prompt and competent medical attention when they appear, follow proper procedures to protect themselves and others when ill, and take the time to recuperate. They should know how to select competent medical advisers and how to find reliable health and consumer information. They need to understand and obey laws that have been passed to protect the health and lives of citizens. They should also study the causes, symptoms, prevention, control, and care of cancer, diabetes, alcoholism, mental illnesses, heart diseases, and various communicable diseases, and understand the relationship between accidents, physical condition, fatigue, alcohol, and emotional status.

They must learn to prepare food and provide some care for the ill, and they need to assume responsibility for applying first aid procedures.

They must also learn and observe practices that protect themselves and others from health hazards in the home, on part-time jobs, on the highway, and while hunting, swimming, or engaging in other recreational pursuits. And they must encourage others to do likewise. They must understand what safety and health hazards are associated with various types of employment and living conditions and recognize the importance of improving these conditions for all people everywhere.

Personal care. Personal appearance is important to them. They fear losing status because of defects in their physical builds, facial features, complexions, or wardrobes. Some try to get attention through extreme types of dress and make-up. They may select and pay for some of their clothes.

Needs. They should receive individual and group counseling concerning appropriate clothing and personal appearance for work, school, play, and social functions.

Intellectual, emotional, social. Youngsters at this age can give more sustained attention to study and can explore problems in greater depth. Cause and effect relationships interest them. For the most part they think in concrete rather than abstract terms. Their speaking ability is more advanced than their reasoning power.

They desire to establish themselves as independent adults and begin to exhibit greater self-control, to accept more responsibility, and to be more cooperative. They often feel insecure and want to assure themselves of personal worth. Some overwork or become perfectionists, some attempt to escape pressures for success, and some try to gain status through exaggerated adult behavior. Delinquency, smoking, drinking, and psychoneurotic conditions increase.

They have high ideals, tend to support the underdog, and dream of a better world.

More permanent friendships develop and interest in the opposite sex mounts. "Going steady" becomes commonplace and some pupils contemplate marriage. They want adult information concerning sex, and they are concerned about their future vocations, army service, college careers and marriage plans.

Needs.   Senior high school students need opportunities to make decisions and to exercise their widening and deepening capacity to think and reason. They need guidance that will help them to appraise their personal strengths and weaknesses, to set attainable goals and strive to achieve them, and to make a wholesome and realistic adjustment to nonremediable limitations.

They require information about the influence of heredity and environment and the fallacies of some common beliefs. They must appreciate the importance of the family in society, the responsibilities and satisfactions that come with establishing a home, and the important factors to consider when selecting a mate. They must appreciate the wonders of creation and the care and love that their parents have given them. They should be given opportunities to earn money and to spend it wisely, and opportunities to associate with the opposite sex and to win acceptance in groups in which they desire to achieve status. They must learn to express their emotions in socially acceptable ways. They should learn that it is better for them to refrain from smoking, drinking, and the improper use of drugs. They need to learn how to handle social situations when they do not want to submit to group pressures.

They should learn to approach personal problems with adequate reflection and have opportunities to make decisions and take appropriate action. They need to associate closely with adults other than parents and to be treated by the family as young adults.

Senior High School
Health and Safety Curriculum

When planning health learning experiences for senior high school pupils, educators endeavor to provide for immediate health needs and also for those that will arise in adult life.

Dating. Learning how to make a wholesome and satisfactory adjustment to the opposite sex is a crucial concern of youths.

1. Invite outside experts to guide discussions of teenage problems: etiquette, dating behavior, driving, hours, drinking, juvenile delinquency, and suitable recreation.

2. Have the students view movies, read articles, and create skits that reveal appropriate and inappropriate ways to become acquainted with members of the opposite sex, to make introductions, to converse with age mates, and to behave in a restaurant or at the theater.

3. Have the students make a handbook of free and inexpensive entertainment that is available in the community, and participate in establishing or improving some youth recreation project. Have them make a checklist of the behavior and appearance that each sex expects of the other and have them rate themselves as "date-bait." Discuss the value of dating as a preparation for marriage.

Marriage and family life. Pupils also need to prepare for the marital responsibilities that they will eventually assume. The teacher should therefore have them:

1. Construct a checklist of factors that one should consider when choosing a friend or mate.

2. Make a self-evaluative checklist of characteristics, attitudes, and abilities one must possess before he is ready to establish a satisfying marriage.

3. Study laws relating to marriage and divorce; conduct panel discussions under the leadership of specialists concerning early marriages, working wives, causes of divorce, and the effect that divorce has on the participants, children, and society.

4. List agencies that offer family- and child-service programs and through interviews, speakers, and field trips ascertain what, when, where, and how the services are rendered.

5. Have the pupils practice modern home nursing techniques and learn how to improvise equipment economically; investigate local agencies that aid in caring for the ill at home; prepare displays of a well-equipped family medicine chest, car first aid kit, or disaster survival shelves, and indicate the cost of the items.

6. Develop a checklist of health and safety factors to consider when

selecting and establishing a home; invite contractors, building inspectors, and home economists to discuss home cost and care and family budgeting; study housing conditions and problems that existed in the past and those that exist today in other countries; examine proposed plans for public and private housing that are under study.

7. List the satisfactions and responsibilities of parenthood after discussing the problems with adults of various ages.

8. Study human reproduction, prenatal care, and how heredity and environment affect human development; report on Mendel's genetic theory and Pavlov's experiments.

9. Make out menus and a grocery list for a week and itemize the cost; evaluate menus on basis of cost, required nutrients, variety, and suitability for needs; list alternative foods to be used that would be less costly and equally nutritious.

10. Organize a class project to provide food, clothing, or medical care for children at home or in a foreign country.

Consumer education. Throughout their lives youths will have to make many choices concerning the selection of health products and services. The teacher may help them make wiser decisions by allowing them to:

1. Establish criteria based on approved standards for selecting a doctor, dentist, and hospital.

2. Compile a list of agencies and publications that provide reliable health information or protect the public from quacks and unsafe health, food, or cosmetic products, and gain an understanding—through books, field trips, interviews, and speakers—of the work that each agency does and how citizens can help them.

3. Explore with specialists the importance of obtaining life, accident, and health insurance. Study the advantages and disadvantages of installment plan buying; evaluate various types of insurance and installment plans; investigate the provisions made for the ill and aged in earlier periods of history, in other countries, and new plans that are being proposed.

4. Discuss the dangers of self-diagnosis and medication, food and diet fads, quack practitioners, and health superstitions; collect supporting evidence from newspapers, laymen, and health workers; read stories about famous quacks and patent medicine kings.

5. Collect food labels and prices from various products; analyze the information; compare size, amount, and quality of products.

6. List various planning, purchasing, and use techniques that a housewife can employ to get the best food and clothing value for her money.

7. Discuss the importance of evaluating health information on the basis of scientific validity and reliability of source.

8. Survey and evaluate the health information presented in an evening on television shows or in a magazine or in a newspaper.

9. Present sociodramas concerning gullible and competent consumers.

Alcohol and drugs. Students may make wiser decisions concerning the use of alcohol and drugs if they are allowed to:

1. List reasons why teenagers drink, use sleeping pills, or experiment with drugs and discuss possible solutions for each.

2. Write scientific articles or radio sketches concerning the effect that improper use of drugs and alcohol has upon the body, mind, emotions, and behavior.

3. Demonstrate through sociodramas appropriate and inappropriate methods of solving problems and meeting disappointments.

4. Invite clergymen, doctors, social workers, or physical educators to discuss techniques for relieving tension; their experiences with alcoholics and drug addicts; the relationship between the improper use of alcohol and drugs and mental and physical illnesses, delinquency, crime, accidents, family happiness, social status, divorce, and the ability to hold a job.

5. Illustrate graphically the amount of food, medicine, travel, clothing, or recreation that can be obtained for the cost of one or more bottles of liquor.

6. Discuss ways to refuse a drink and to avoid drinking situations.

7. Study laws governing the manufacture, sale, and use of alcohol and drugs; investigate what is being done from local to international levels to educate people about alcoholism and drugs, to prevent addiction, and to rehabilitate addicts.

8. Invite a bus driver, aviator, or employer to discuss company policies and attitudes concerning alcoholism.

Driver education. During these years youths establish driving habits that protect or endanger their lives and those of other people. Hence, this is an opportune time for the teacher to encourage them to:

1. Examine the construction of a car and how it operates; study the fundamentals of starting, stopping, shifting, steering, parking, signaling, backing, and turning a car around.

2. Invite experts to discuss factors to consider when purchasing a car, laws pertaining to the driving and ownership of vehicles, and the cost of car operation and maintenance.

3. Interview people to discover what problems they encountered after an accident: difficulties at the scene of the accident, hospital and rehabilitation experiences, medical bills, loss of income, physical disability, law suits, and loss of loved ones.

4. Analyze factors that have contributed to recent accidents: poor health, fatigue, drinking, speed, law violations, road or weather conditions, emotional status, and pedestrian behavior.

5. Illustrate (through diagrams, cartoons, posters, radio skits, or dramatizations): what to do at the scene of an accident; how to meet various emergencies; how to drive under different weather, road, and lighting conditions; how to interpret road signs and driver signals.

6. Visit traffic courts, trials involving accidents, license bureaus, driving ranges, and inspection stations.

7. Make graphs showing accident trends, the comparisons of deaths from automobile accidents and various diseases, the age of drivers involved in accidents.

CHAPTER VI

Methods of Teaching Health and Safety

Because a classroom teacher plays a crucial role in determining what and how children are taught, he should know how to select and develop units of study, to identify those factors which affect learning, and to utilize different teaching materials and methods.

Units of Study and Lesson Plans

A knowledge of the patterns of child growth and development and the goals of health education provide a guide for the process of selecting and constructing units. Prepared courses of study and various professional publications also give helpful guidance, but borrowing readymade lesson plans from any source is inadvisable. Because children and communities differ, each class needs somewhat different learning experiences. Thus, each semester the teacher must ask two questions: What do these *particular* pupils need to learn about health? What materials and methods of presentation will help them acquire these knowledges, skills, attitudes, and behaviors most quickly and effectively?

To answer these questions, the teacher must collect considerable information about the health needs, problems, interests, and beliefs of his pupils and the community (see pp. 31 and 73). Before making a final decision about what to teach, the teacher should also review the local and state health education requirements; examine the available teaching guides and resources; and find out what pupils have studied in previous health classes, what they may study in succeeding years, and what they will be studying concurrently in other classes.

This preliminary survey produces the data that an instructor needs to select appropriate health units and to make intelligent decisions concerning the various aspects of the unit plans: (1) the approach, (2) the objectives, (3) the content, and (4) the evaluative techniques.

Approaches.   Igniting interest in a unit and getting pupils to feel that it is of vital importance to them—that it is their problem rather than the teacher's problem—requires considerable professional skill. The more the teacher knows about the background and interests of his students, their health status and needs, the nature of their community, and current issues that concern them and their families, the easier he will find this process. The outbreak of an epidemic, an accident at a nearby farm or factory, or a casual question asked in class may present a golden opportunity for introducing a unit. Curiosity and concern about a problem may also be aroused through stimulating outside speakers, movies, or field trips. Whatever approach is used, the purpose is not merely to entertain pupils, but rather to make them eager to participate in the learning experience because they see that it will be of value to them.

Objectives.   Rushing headlong into learning activities after formulating a general concept of what is to be achieved is a mistake. It pays the teacher to pause and probe until he can stipulate precisely what skills, understandings, and attitudes pupils are to acquire. If the objective of the unit is "to improve students' dental health practices," it is difficult to decide how to attain this nebulous goal and how to evaluate whether it has been achieved. But, if the objective is "to get pupils to brush their teeth after each meal, to have cavities filled, and to know what foods cause decay," the opposite is true. The more specific and realistic the unit objectives are, the more likely they are to be realized. Teachers cannot arbitrarily set up rigid standards and goals regardless of existing environmental conditions and of the varying abilities among students. Grandiose, generalized goals may appear impressive on paper, but they usually produce disappointing results in the classroom.

Content.   An instructor does considerable preplanning for a unit, but he draws pupils into the process as soon and as much as possible. Together they may define and delimit their problem, divide it into major topics and subtopics, and decide how to culminate the unit. After discussing various activities and materials that might help them probe each topic, they endeavor to select those that will make the greatest contribution to the realization of their objectives. Since chaos can result if no definite plans are made for carrying out these activities, they also (1) decide in what order to develop various aspects of the unit; (2) delegate responsibilities to groups and individuals, define the nature of their duties, and set "due-dates"; (3) ascertain where equipment and supplies are available and plan how to obtain, set up, distribute, share, collect, and return them; (4) decide where activities are to take place and how to get to and from these areas; and (5) plan how to modify the program if a film delivery is delayed or an outside speaker is unable to appear.

Evaluation.   The teacher must also select or construct evaluative techniques that will help him diagnose pupils' problems and measure their progress. Pretests and interviews with pupils, parents, and the school nurse or doctor may be helpful. The students may engage in self- and group evaluations. Mastery of the unit objectives can be measured by administering knowledge, skill, or attitude tests. Follow-up procedures can be planned to check whether pupils' practices improve as a result of instruction and whether impairments are corrected. (A more complete discussion of evaluation is presented in Chapter VIII.)

Daily lesson plans.   When a unit is underway, a teacher drafts lesson plans to provide a detailed, daily instructional guide. To do this, he mentally reviews what was done during the preceding periods, outlines activities for the next one, estimates the amount of time that each activity will consume, and decides on the order of their presentation. Before meeting the class, he obtains the necessary instructional materials, sets up the required equipment, and plans efficient work procedures. If any ideas for improving instruction spring to his mind during a lesson, he notes them for future reference. Neither the daily lesson plans nor the unit plans are regarded as inflexible; an instructor revises them and introduces new ideas whenever it seems prudent to do so.

Factors that Affect Learning

The amount of learning that takes place in a classroom depends upon three factors: the learner, the learning task, and the teaching procedures.

Character of the learner.   Heredity, environment, maturity, and motivation are largely responsible for determining what a student can and will learn.

Heredity.   Because children differ in genetic endowment, they differ in intelligence, specific aptitudes, and constitutional equipment. Consequently, the teacher cannot prod all of them through the same learning maze at the same pace. The instructional process must be geared so that each child can develop his potentialities to the highest level and can learn to make a wholesome adjustment to his limitations.

Environment.   The genes set limits on and provide the potential for development, but it is the home, the school, and the community that determine whether youngsters cultivate their capacities. Thus, as has been previously noted, a teacher must make inquiries concerning the environmental forces that impinge upon pupils: What discipline, guidance, and physical care have they received? What recreational, cultural, travel, work, and academic activities have they experienced? Where and how do they study? What is the social and economic status of their families? What is the quality of their relationships with parents, siblings, teachers, and other students? What health, safety, and moral conditions exist in their homes and community? What is the nature of the local terrain, climate, and natural resources? A probe of this nature will indicate whether or not it is feasible or prudent to present a particular learning task. It will reveal whether there exist deleterious conditions that need to be eradicated. It will disclose what learning experiences and health services pupils need most in order to cope with their environment.

Whether or not pupils learn depends not only on the environment but also upon how they view the world and themselves. As a result of their home and community contacts they formulate definite concepts about their health, appearance, abilities, deficiencies, opportunities, and status in the home and school. They also draw conclusions concerning what is right and wrong and what is of the greatest and least importance in life. These concepts color what students perceive in the classroom: Because of these views, they may ignore incoming stimuli, consider them of utmost importance, judge them objectively, distort them to conform to their beliefs, or dismiss them as beyond their potential. When working with students, therefore, it is important to discover what mental pictures they have of themselves and their world, and, if necessary, to help them make more realistic appraisals. Not uncommonly the teacher has to provide for considerable "unlearning" before new learning can take place.

Maturity.   Learning and growth are progressive and inextricably bound together. A child cannot master a learning task unless the organs and systems of his body are sufficiently mature to function as required by the task. What he can learn is dependent not only upon his physical development, but also upon his intellectual, social, and emotional development, and these aspects of growth do not necessarily proceed at the same rate. A pupil may mature physically, for example, much more rapidly than he does socially, and this uneven growth pattern must be taken into consideration when planning learning experiences for him.

All children experience a similar sequence of growth but because of their heredity and environment they do not all develop at the same rate or to the same extent. A wide range of individual differences is found in each class. Thus, it is imperative that the teacher include various levels and types of materials, activities, and objectives in health units so that each student can experience some measure of growth, success, and satisfaction.

Motivation. Some pupils from a favorable environment who are generously endowed genetically are poorer achievers than classmates who possess modest abilities. What causes this? It appears that the type and amount of learning that a person will do depends, in part, upon how highly motivated he is to learn. A motive is not something that is presented to youngsters, but rather a driving force that exists within them that arises out of biological and social needs, such as the desire to win approval, to avoid pain, and to associate with others. No simple prescription can be given for linking health instruction to pupils' motives, for their needs change as they mature and their environment changes. Several youngsters may master the same learning task for different motives. A child may perform a health practice for different reasons at different times and may terminate it whenever a stronger, rival motive captures his attention. A health educator must keep in mind that each "child's motives are intrinsically his own, useful if they can be tapped, malleable if guided, but resistant if thwarted."[1]

Nature of the task.   The nature of the learning task also plays a role in determining how much and how rapidly pupils will learn.

Difficulty of the task.   Children are more apt to tackle a lesson if it is sufficiently beyond their level of ability to present an interest-

---

[1] Howard L. Kingsley and Ralph Garry, *The Nature and Conditions of Learning,* 2nd ed. (Englewood Cliffs, N.J.: Prentice-Hall, Inc., 1957), p. 191.

ing challenge, but not so difficult that the objective appears to be unattainable. If an assignment is exceptionally easy, they may become bored and seek other outlets for their energies. If it is extremely difficult, they may become discouraged and terminate all effort to learn.

How can the teacher judge whether or not a task will be difficult for students? In general, the more complex a lesson is and the more material it contains, the longer it will take to master it. This condition can be somewhat overcome, however, if the material is meaningful or familiar. Three lines of poetry or coherent prose, are easier to grasp, for example, than three lines of nonsense syllables. Thus, a teacher is constantly confronted with the problem of finding ways of making unfamiliar material meaningful to students.

Education is a step-by-step process: new knowledges are built upon the skills and information that one already possesses. Students cannot understand morbidity tables, for example, if they have not mastered certain numerical concepts. If they cannot connect new, unfamiliar learning materials with their previous experiences in some way, they become lost in a meaningless maze. They cannot learn, for they do not have any clues or tools that will help them solve their problems. If a teacher can show them that a relationship exists between a new concept and a pattern of knowledge that they already possess, a segment of a lesson may suddenly snap into meaningful focus for them. This quickly attained measure of success will delight students and will encourage them to proceed with the remainder of the lesson.

Environment of the task.   If the teacher is enthusiastic and well-informed about his subject and establishes a congenial and stimulating pupil-teacher and pupil-pupil relationships, he creates a classroom climate that is conducive to learning. If the study area is attractive and clean and the ventilation, heating, and lighting are properly controlled, pupils do better work. The amount of noise and distraction that exists in the classroom, the quantity and quality of books and other resources that are available, and the amount of time and freedom that is allotted to complete tasks also affect learning.

Understanding the task.   Vaguely defined learning tasks hamper learning. If the objectives of a lesson and means of achieving them are not made perfectly clear, students waste time fumbling about searching for direction and become disturbed because they do not know exactly where or how to apply their efforts. Conversely, if initial instructions delineate the essential elements and relationships involved in a task and the correct pattern of responses required to achieve the stipulated goal, the pupils will proceed to master it more efficiently. They will develop fewer bad habits that must be overcome, will experience less boredom and emotional blockage, and will be more apt to complete the assignment.

Nature of teaching procedures.   Some teaching methods produce more effective learning than others.

Variety.   Since pupils must pay attention if they are to learn and since novelty and change are means of securing and maintaining attention, it is prudent to spice learning experiences with variety. Providing for a change of approach, pace, materials, and methods from unit to unit, from day to day, and even within a class period does much to leaven learning.

Practice schedules.   In most instances, pupils master tasks more quickly and easily if practice periods are distributed—spaced—rather than massed. This is particularly true if a task is complex, not particularly meaningful, or requires the expenditure of considerable effort.

When spaced practice periods are scheduled, the length of the practice and rest sessions must be carefully gauged. It is usually best to schedule short practice periods for young children and difficult materials. The periods may be longer if the children are older, if the materials are less complicated, or if some mastery has been achieved but greater proficiency is sought. A practice period should be long enough to provide the warmup and orientation that pupils need to complete and repeat one or more patterns of response. It should terminate before their attention wanders and fatigue or boredom causes their performance to deteriorate. The most appropriate length for the rest period varies with the nature of the task and length of the practice period. A long practice period is apt to require a long rest period. During the initial stages of learning, short practice and rest periods will usually produce the most effective learning; later these periods may be lengthened.

Drill, recitation, review.   Rushing students from one learning task to another as soon as they have attained mastery produces more forgetting and frustration than long-term learning. Youngsters are more apt to retain what they learn if they *overlearn* it, that is if they repeat the task after the first effortless performance of it. But prolonging drills beyond a certain point produces diminishing returns, and instituting premature drill may fix incorrect responses that are difficult to eradicate.

Reviews and recitations tend to insure greater permanency of learning. Since the most forgetting occurs soon after initial learning, these activities are more useful if scheduled shortly after the original study period and spaced over a period of time. If learning is to become more firmly fixed, however, the same high level of active participation is required during the repetition of a skill as preceded the first correct performance of it.

Whole and part learning.   Will a lesson be learned more quickly if the entire sequence of responses is practiced until mastery is achieved or if segments of the sequence are mastered one at a time? The "whole" method of learning is advantageous because the pupils perceive the associations between the parts and the whole and practice integrating items in the order required for performance. Considerable effort must be expended, however, before the results of their labors can be noted. In the part method, on the other hand, pupils experience a measure of success each time that they master a subgoal and are thus spurred on to further effort. After mastering all of the segments, however, they may have difficulty meshing them together to perform the total task. Sometimes pupils can experience the advantages of both whole and part learning. To do this they first obtain an overview of an entire learning task, then practice segments of it, and finally review it as a whole to fix the entire associative train.

Incentives for learning.   The best incentive that a teacher can supply to facilitate learning is self-incentive. If pupils can be shown that mastering a learning task will satisfy one of their deeply felt needs, they will exert a tremendous amount of effort to achieve the goal. If a task does not seem to be related to their needs or wants, they are apt to ignore it. A number of other incentives will also stimulate learning, but some of them produce undesirable side effects. Pupils will perform a health task to win the approval of a parent or teacher, to avoid criticism or punishment, to terminate nagging, to win a prize, to get a good grade, or to escape group censure. But if they do not see value in performing the task for its own sake, they may cheat or employ other shortcuts that circumvent learning. Also, they may discontinue the health practice as soon as the incentive is removed. Moreover, they may develop an active dislike for health instruction and try to avoid similar activities in the future.

Learning seems to be facilitated if pupils receive information periodically concerning the results of their efforts. Awareness of some measure of success apparently serves as an incentive to greater effort. Awareness of mistakes enables pupils to judge where they need to apply further effort. Thus, the sooner this information is obtained and the more specific it is, the greater is the improvement in performance. Since raw results are not always meaningful to a pupil, it is often necessary to help them interpret the information and decide what they should do to correct their faults. Learning proceeds more quickly, however, if the teacher gets pupils actively involved in this analysis process.

In general, praise seems to promote learning, but reproof is better than ignoring pupils' progress. Reproof discourages some students and may cause them to terminate their efforts; however, it seems to serve as a satisfactory stimulus to more self-assured youngsters. Blanket health threats and promises may stimulate learning, but they may also produce adverse reactions. Trouble may ensue if a teacher tells pupils that they won't become varsity football players if they don't drink milk or that they won't get poliomyelitis if they get Salk immunization shots. If youngsters know of instances where these statements have not held true, they may feel that the teacher is deceiving them and may become skeptical of everything he says. Better results are usually obtained if pupils are taught how to evaluate the reliability of health information and are permitted to weigh the pros and cons of health issues and to reach their own conclusions.

Methods of Presentation

No teaching media is unconditionally guaranteed to be educational. When health information is poured into passive youngsters, absorption does not automatically take place. Students can be exposed to a textbook, movie, or lecture and learn little or nothing. To learn, they must become actively involved in observing and experimenting, in interpreting information, in searching for relationships, in ordering data, and in applying principles. They are more likely to do this if they have a list of clues or things to look for or listen to before they are exposed to the learning media. They will progress more rapidly if they evaluate their work as they go along and summarize the key points after any presentation.

The pupils must do their own learning; the teacher cannot do it for them. But the teacher can supply materials, questions, suggestions, encouragement, and other stimuli that will keep students actively involved in grasping concepts and mastering skills. It is the teacher's responsibility to select a combination of media and methods of presenting them that will provide for the fullest realization of the unit objectives. To do this, he must be thoroughly familiar with the advantages and disadvantages of each media and the best methods of utilizing them.

Textbooks. The most commonplace teaching tool is the textbook. A single textbook cannot provide adequately for individual differences among children, but it can present considerable information in a compact fashion that will serve as a common core of content and a point of departure and referral for various class activities. If a textbook is carefully selected (see pp. 92-93), if full use is made of its pictures and other teaching aids, and if it is supplemented by other published materials of varying degrees of difficulty and audio-visual aids, it can contribute significantly to learning experiences.

Workbooks and programmed learning materials permit pupils to work at their own pace and free the teacher for more individual guidance. If a workbook merely requires pupils to copy items from the textbook, it is useless. If it presents a range of problems that will help youngsters of varied capacities grasp concepts, apply principles, or reinforce what they have learned, it can be of great value. At present, educators are excited about the new programmed learning materials that present a small segment of information, ask pupils a question based on that information, and then reveal the correct answer. A child works at his own pace and constantly contributes. He immediately receives information about his results which reinforces what he has learned and his success stimulates him to take the next step. Each step builds upon the preceding one and thus helps the child grasp a more complex concept. If programmed learning materials are properly structured, they can facilitate the mastery of some types of health concepts. When teaching machines are required, of course, greater expense is involved.

Lectures and speeches.   Blanket denunciations of lectures are not justified. They may be more teacher-centered than pupil-centered, but these drawbacks can be somewhat overcome. Logically organized lectures that are skillfully related to pupils' needs and interests and delivered with infectious enthusiasm will promote learning. It is best to use them sparingly, however—perhaps to introduce a unit, to summarize a lesson, or to illustrate a point. If the meaning of the spoken word is reinforced by the introduction of tactile, auditory, or visual experiences, and if pupils are given opportunities to ask questions, better results are obtained.

A class can also benefit from a lecture that is given by a student or adult in the community. If an adult is asked to lecture, the teacher should check to see whether he is an interesting speaker and whether he knows how to work with youngsters. The teacher may make the preliminary contact with the guest to explain what is desired and to inform him about the age and interests of the youngsters. The pupils will learn more if they prepare questions to ask the speaker, introduce him, and write the notes of invitation and thanks.

Class discussion.   Stimulating class discussions can spark intensive interest in health problems. When they are purposefully guided, pupils often obtain insights and develop attitudes and plans for action that they could not achieve in any other way. Haphazard interchanges of ideas among pupils, on the other hand, can degenerate into boring and fruitless ordeals. Worthwhile discussions are more likely to take place if instructors:

1. Frame discussion topics that require the presentation of different points of view rather than the reproduction of the "right" answer.
2. Maintain an objective and impartial attitude and make certain that each point of view is given a full and fair hearing.[2]
3. Provide exploratory questions and reading materials that help pupils build a sufficient reservoir of knowledge to make intelligent comments.
4. Draw every pupil into active participation; keep a participation check list and post it to elicit more responses from timid students and to curb the loquacious ones.
5. Refrain from supplying too much information; get pupils to think by having them clarify statements, probe points more deeply, expand

2 Fred V. Hein, "Teaching Controversial Issues in Health Education," *Journal of Health, Physical Education, and Recreation,* 32 (October, 1961), 19.

the scope of their discussion, search for relationships, evaluate divergent points of view, defend positions, spot inaccuracies, and search for overlooked facts or conditions.

6. Give pupils time to deliberate before making replies and get them to listen critically and respectfully to classmates.

7. Help pupils establish criteria for judging the reliability of health information and encourage them to apply these standards at all times.

8. Make encouraging comments, commend helpful contributions, and avoid embarrassing students who make inept responses.

9. Keep the discussion to the point and govern its pace and tone; use appropriate facial expressions, vocal inflections, and gestures; ask logically ordered questions; and have pupils periodically evaluate the quality and progress of their work.

10. Jot pupils' comments on the blackboard; have them group, weigh, and order the items and then have them decide what step needs to be taken next to reach their objectives.

11. Divide the class into small committees, panels, or buzz groups to provide for more leadership opportunities, a better coverage of ideas, and a wider sharing of decision making; stay in the background to evaluate proceedings and offer guidance; have each committee summarize its findings for the class.

Models, displays, graphic materials, and other media.   Some tactile and visual experiences may help students grasp a concept more quickly and clearly than will oral or printed words. Consequently, health educators frequently use three-dimensional models of body organs and actual objects, such as teeth, bones, and medical equipment. Physiological, anatomical, nutritional, and first aid charts, tables, diagrams, and graphs can help convey considerable information in a compact form. Cartoons, posters, bulletin board displays, and showcase exhibits can capture the attention of students and convey messages that are not quickly forgotten. These media may be purchased, borrowed, or constructed by the teacher or pupils. When youngsters make them, they take great pride in seeing them exhibited.

Audiovisual media.   Audiovisual media supplement and enrich the usual classroom presentations. They often convey ideas more effectively than other media, because they use more than one kind of stimulus—color, sound, printed symbols, action sequences—to interpret, clarify and correlate subject matter. Moreover, audiovisual presentations bring isolated classes into contact with outstanding health authorities and master teachers who can provide a wealth of enriching experiences. A movie can depict past and present events and local and distant places in a relatively brief amount of time and can present dangerous and complicated demonstrations in a safe and economical manner. It can speed up or slow down time and reduce or increase the size of objects to emphasize procedures, processes, or principles. It may employ a complex of models, diagrams, animated illustrations, exhibits, and laboratory equipment that the local school cannot afford to supply.

Drawbacks as well as advantages are associated with the use of audiovisual resources. Some of the materials and equipment are expensive and some are of inferior quality. It may be difficult or impossible to preview them or to synchronize the timing of the presentation with the current class topic. One-way communication hinders learning, for pupils cannot ask questions of the media and the media cannot adapt the pace and presentation to the reaction of students.

Some of these drawbacks can be overcome. A teacher can make tape recordings of health programs or commercials and present them whenever it is appropriate. He can rerun or stop a film to discuss, review, or re-examine certain points. Some radio and television stations and agencies supply helpful study guides and previews of their programs or movies. Some textbook writers and curriculum constructors correlate textbooks and courses of study with films and filmstrips and also provide instructional guidebooks. Some of the new recording projectors and films are designed so that one can add comments to films and later erase them. This makes it possible for an instructor to supply a sound track that will meet the needs of a particular class.

Filmstrips which have a number of still pictures on a continuous strip of film are relatively inexpensive and can be advanced through the projector by hand at a speed that is most suitable for the pupils. Slides are inexpensive and can be selected and arranged in the order that is most desirable for a lesson. Overhead and opaque projectors enable a teacher to present pictures, pages of a book, copies of students' work, and typed materials.

Audiovisual materials are more useful learning tools if the teacher critically previews them, selects only those that will make the most significant contribution to the unit objectives, and correlates the presentation with the unit content. It is important to place orders for equipment and materials well in advance of usage, to check whether they function properly upon arrival, and to have them set up and ready for presentation when the class arrives.

Demonstrations and experiments.   Students often grasp concepts and reach convictions more quickly through direct observation of concrete situations than through any other means. A three-dimensional "live" demonstration, for example, may present movement, position, or spatial relations more clearly than a two-dimensional book, film, or picture. Moreover, the teacher can gear the pace of the demonstration to the needs of the pupils and can repeat steps or answer questions whenever necessary.

Demonstrations and experiments can show procedures, techniques, or cause and effect relationships. They are particularly useful when teaching home nursing, first aid, or health and safety practices. To present an effective demonstration, the teacher should observe the following practices:

1. Before meeting the class, run through the demonstration to insure that each step is included and placed in the proper sequence and that all materials are functioning properly and organized for the most efficient usage.

2. Remove all distractions and make certain that every pupil can see and hear what is going on. Sometimes it is best to have them view the demonstration from the position that they will perform the task themselves.

3. Keep the experiment or demonstration simple and verbalization at a minimum. Give clear, brief explanations just prior to performing each step. Concentrate on *what* to do during the demonstration. Refrain from supplying pupils with all of the answers; make them observe and draw their own conclusions.

4. Immediately after a demonstration, have pupils practice the procedures and evaluate their efforts. Encourage them to apply their knowledge in a real-life situation as soon as possible.

Field trips.   Field trips bring pupils into exciting, real-life contacts with their community and satisfy their natural desire to explore. They enable students to acquire accurate, firsthand knowledge about things that cannot be brought into the classroom. They consume considerable time, however, and poorly planned trips can become holidays from learning that turn into fiascos.

The more actively pupils participate in planning field trips and in carrying them out, the more they learn. They can prepare a list of questions to ask and observations to make; contact their hosts and make arrangements with them; investigate the cost, route, and methods of transportation; and establish group behavior standards and procedures. After returning from a trip, it is important for them to evaluate and summarize the experience in some form so as to integrate and reinforce what they have learned.

Rather than take class time for field trips, it may be advisable to have individuals or committees undertake specific trips or interviews. This method can provide for a broader coverage of areas relating to a health problem, and all students can benefit if the committees bring back written reports or tape recordings of their visits.

Dramatization.   Because children love to play, to pretend, and to mimic others, dramatization is a useful teaching tool, particularly on the elementary school level. A few published plays are available, but usually it is best to have children create their own as an outgrowth of class activities. Brief sociodramas and spontaneous improvisations are especially suitable for approaching human relations problems. Closely akin to plays are health pantomimes, puppet shows, shadow plays, quizzes, and "radio" and "television" programs.

Pupils can profit from selecting and integrating information to dramatize health principles. When acting out their parts, they reveal their personal viewpoints and how meaningful the subject matter covered in class has been to them. When playing the roles of parents, bus drivers, or handicapped persons, they become more conscious of other people's problems, viewpoints, and feelings and may develop more favorable attitudes toward them. Moreover, acting cultivates creativity, strengthens cooperative skills, gives a shy child a way of forgetting himself, provides an attention-seeker with a legitimate access to the limelight. But dramatizations can also deprive pupils of adequate health instruction. This occurs when only a few gifted students take part and when the emphasis is placed on perfection of performance rather than upon the reinforcement and clarification of health concepts.

Problem-solving.   Pupils will have to solve health problems throughout their lives; hence, they should acquire experience in doing it while in school. This may be done on an individual or group basis. Some problems may be of a personal nature: Should I smoke? Should I become a doctor? Other problems may be of a social nature: How can we reduce accidents on the playground? How should we behave at school parties?

Through the process of problem-solving pupils cultivate their creative capacities, sharpen their critical thinking skills, and improve their individual and group work habits. Moreover, they become accustomed to assuming responsibility and to making and acting upon decisions. Problem-solving is time-consuming, however, and cannot be done successfully unless pupils receive expert guidance as they: (1) select a problem that is of direct concern to them; (2) clarify and limit the problem which may require that they interview people, make a survey, or engage in other exploratory activities; (3) suggest various solutions for the problem and decide which appears to be the most logical and prudent; (4) recall information that bears on the proposed solution and determine what added data are required and where it can be found; (5) accumulate the information through observation, reading, surveys, experiments, or other means; (6) evaluate the data, weigh and order it, analyze and interpret it, and draw conclusions from it; and (7) apply the conclusions to a life situation.

Group problem-solving may range from a brief informal analysis of a situation by a committee to a unit of instruction that involves several weeks of work. Some problem-solving activities culminate in elaborate undertakings such as cleanup, safety, or fire prevention campaigns; posture clinics; foot health programs; diabetes detection programs; the establishment of recreation centers; and the development of service projects in hospitals, schools, or the community.

Students often turn to a trusted teacher for advice concerning their personal health problems and some schools routinely schedule guidance conferences at the time that health examinations are given. These conferences are usually more productive if the instructor examines pertinent health and cumulative records beforehand, arranges for private interviews, and listens sympathetically. His task is not to tell students what to do, but rather to help them clarify and analyze their problems and locate the information or specialists to solve them. A health teacher helps students collect and interpret data, examine various courses of action, and consider the probable consequences of each choice, but leaves the final decision up to them and to their parents. He keeps a record of each conference, checks progress, and gives encouragement and guidance.

CHAPTER VII

Resources for Instruction

Keeping informed about the ever-increasing supply of instructional resources is the responsibility of teachers; obtaining funds to acquire an adequate supply of them is the duty of administrators. Among the specialists on the school staff who can assist in this work are the health and audiovisual aids coordinators, librarians, nurses, doctors, dentists, speech therapists, psychologists, dental hygienists, and visiting teachers. These staff members may suggest available sources of materials, give advice concerning pupils' health problems, provide information about new knowledges in their field, evaluate the scientific accuracy of health education materials, or serve as classroom speakers.

Guides to Resources

Several guides may be used to locate instructional materials: the library card catalogue, the *Education Index,* the *Readers' Guide to Periodical Literature,* the *Cumulative Book Index,* and the *New York Times Index.* Two other useful searching tools are the *Guide to Reference Books,* by Constance Winchell, and *How to Locate Educational Information and Data,* by Carter Alexander and Arvid Burke.

Courses and units of study. The courses of study, units, and guides that the school system and state department of education provide should give one the best clues concerning resources that are available locally. Examining similar materials that other agencies publish and the health units that appear in professional journals and textbooks is also advisable. The Association for Supervision and Curriculum Development (National Education Association) compiles an annual list of instructional guides that state departments of education, school systems, and colleges produce; and the *Education Index* lists course of study under that heading.

The following are examples of items that can be obtained from state departments of education:

Commonwealth of Massachusetts, Boston. *A Guide to Teaching Health in Massachusetts Junior High Schools,* 1956.

Commonwealth of Virginia, Richmond. *Health Education, Grades 8–12,* 1956.

California, Sacramento. *Teachers Guide to Education in Later Childhood,* 1957; *Teachers Guide in Health Education for Secondary Schools,* 1952.

Florida, Tallahassee. *Better Health for Florida's Children,* 1957.

Indiana, Indianapolis. *A Guide for Health Education in Indiana Schools,* Bulletin No. 219, 1956.

Kansas, Topeka. *A Curriculum Guide for Elementary Schools of Kansas,* 1958.

Michigan, Lansing. *The Michigan Driver Education Manual,* Bulletin No. 360, 1956.

Oregon, Salem. *Handbook for Health Instruction in Oregon Elementary Schools,* 1952. *Health Materials and Resources for Oregon Teachers.* Oregon, 1962.

University of the State of New York, Albany. *Guide to the Teaching of Health in the Elementary School,* 1946; *Health Teaching Syllabus for the Junior and Senior High Schools,* 1958, and its supplement, *Instruction Regarding Narcotics and Habit-Forming Drugs,* 1960.

Methods and materials books. Teaching methods books provide a wealth of information about teaching materials and how to use them. They usually give an overview of health education; discuss the development of health units and give detailed examples; provide many suggestions for field trips, demonstrations, surveys, and other activities; and list the sources and names of specific films, books, pamphlets, and materials that are useful. Many of these books are listed in the bibliography (see items 2, 7, 8, 9, 10, 11, 13, 14, 15, 19, 20, 22, 23, 24, 25, 26, 27, 28, 29).

Textbooks for students. There are elementary and secondary school health textbooks, series, and workbooks on the market. Teaching manuals that contain a wealth of worthwhile suggestions are available for many of them. One can obtain information about textbooks from publishers, professional journals, and the *Cumulative Book Index.* A convenient source for locating elementary and secondary texts is *Textbooks in Print* (formerly the *American Educational Catalog*), an annual publication which normally appears in April. It lists new, revised, and in-print books under subject headings, but the listings are not annotated. Some universities have extensive collections of textbooks that are open to examination.

Free and inexpensive teaching aids. An abundance of free and inexpensive teaching aids can be obtained if the teacher knows how to locate them. Professional journals often give information about new items, and the *Education Index* lists many pamphlets. Other sources that can be consulted are:

1. *The Vertical File Index,* a monthly publication which lists pamphlets, charts, posters, and other materials that are currently available (but it usually does not include United States government publications).

2. *The Elementary Teacher's Guide to Free Curriculum Materials,* published annually by Educators Progress Service, Box 4975, Randolf, Wisconsin.

3. *Free and Inexpensive Learning Materials,* published annually by the Division of Surveys and Field Services, George Peabody College for Teachers, Nashville, Tennessee.

4. *Free and Inexpensive Health Instruction Materials,* edited by John R. LeFevre and Donald N. Boydston and published by Southern Illinois University Press, Carbondale, Illinois.

5. *A Guidebook Describing Pamphlets, Posters, Films, on Health and Disease* by Perry F. Prather, M.D., Baltimore: Maryland State Department of Health, 1960.

Audiovisual aids. A health educator should first become familiar with the audiovisual aids that the local school has purchased and those that can be obtained from community agencies, the state health and education departments, and nearby institutions of higher learning. Professional journals, textbooks, teachers' manuals, resource units, courses of study, and the following sources will help him locate others:

1. *Educational Film Guide; Filmstrip Guide,* H. W. Wilson Company, New York, N.Y.

2. *Educators Guide to Free Films; Educators Guide to Free Slide-Films; Educators Guide to Free Tapes, Scripts, and Transcriptions,* Educators Progress Service, Box 497, Randolf, Wisconsin.

3. *Motion Pictures and Filmstrips; Music and Phonorecords,* National Union Catalogue, Library of Congress, Washington, D. C.

4. *Blue Book of Audio-Visual Materials,* a special issue of *Educational Screen,* lists films, film strips, slides, and recordings.

5. *Visual Materials in Safety Education, Supplement II; A Bibliography,* National Commission on Safety Education, Washington, D. C.

6. Slides can be obtained from the Society for Visual Education, 1345 Diversey Parkway, Chicago 14, Illinois.

7. *National Tape Recording Catalog,* Department of Audio-Visual Instruction, National Education Association, Washington, D. C.

8. *Annotated List of Phonograph Records,* edited by Warren S. Freeman, Children's Reading Service, 1078 St. John's Place, Brooklyn, N.Y.

9. The Children's Record Catalog, Harrison Record Catalogs, Department A, 274 Madison Avenue, New York, N.Y.

10. Free radio scripts can be obtained from the Bureau of Research in Education by Radio, University of Texas, Austin, Texas. The educational kit contains a teacher's manual, evaluation and production manuals, and other items.

Other audio-visual aids, such as models, posters, graphic materials, specimens, display and demonstration materials, and laboratory equipment can be purchased from a number of companies. Many items can be obtained at little or no cost from many state and federal government agencies and voluntary health agencies; insurance companies and commercial concerns; local doctors, dentists, druggists, and merchants; and school science, home economics, and physical education departments. Checklists and advertisements in health journals will help the teacher locate many of the items that are available.

Agencies that Provide Resources

Helping hands are extended to health educators by numerous agencies. The services vary. Agencies may conduct research programs, compile reports and statistical information, establish standards and policies, or publish journals and pamphlets. They may supply funds or leadership for health workshops, conferences, training programs, demonstrations, or special projects. Some agencies maintain film and record libraries and prepare bibliographies, health units, resource guides, posters, exhibits, and other teaching materials. They may also offer consultant or technical services, supply speakers, or permit students to visit their laboratories, plants, or institutions.

Agencies that operate on the local, state, and national levels usually prefer that schools make contacts and order items through the local unit. Upon request, some of them will send an instructor a catalog of their materials and will place his name on their mailing lists. The teacher must consult the most recent price lists and catalogs, for some materials are offered only for a limited time. Because agencies and business firms sometimes change their names, addresses, and the names of their publications, it is always wise to check the following references for up-to-date information: *Encyclopedia of Associations* (Vol. I: *National Organizations of the United States*) and *Poor's Register of Directors and Executives*.

Professional, voluntary, and special interest groups. A health teacher should become an active member of the professional and voluntary associations that are most closely associated with his work and should become acquainted with the staff and services of other health agencies in the community.

School health associations. Three professional associations are deeply concerned about school health problems. They publish journals, yearbooks, and reports that contain a wealth of up-to-date information and much can be gained from their meetings, conventions, and special services.

The American Association for Health, Physical Education, and Recreation (AAHPER), Washington 6, D. C., publishes the *Journal of Health, Physical Education, and Recreation* and the *Research Quarterly,* as well as numerous other bulletins and books.

The American School Health Association, 515 East Main Street, Kent, Ohio, publishes the *Journal of School Health.*

The American Public Health Association, New York 19, N.Y., which has a School Health Section, publishes the *American Journal of Public Health* and a *Section Newsletter.*

Education associations. A health teacher can also turn to various education associations for assistance. The primary source, of course, is the National Education Association, Washington 6, D. C., which publishes the *National Education Association Journal,* the *Research Bulletin,* and many reports, pamphlets, bibliographies, and other materials.

Several departments of the National Education Association also provide services that aid health teachers: The American Association for Health, Physical Education, and Recreation; Audio-Visual Instruction; Classroom Teachers; International Council for Exceptional Children; Home Economics; Kindergarten–Primary Education; National Science Teachers Association; National Council for the Social Studies; Rural Education; The American Association of School Administrators; Association for Supervision and Curriculum Development; and Elementary School Principals. These departments publish articles in their journals that are of interest to health educators, and some occasionally devote their yearbooks to health topics (see bibliography, items 1, 3, 6).

Safety groups. Teachers who are concerned with safety education will want to become familiar with the many publications, audiovisual aids, and services that are provided by the National Commission on Safety Education of the National Education Association. Another agency that does outstanding work is the National Safety Council, Chicago, Illinois, which publishes the magazine, *Safety Education,* many teaching guides, and an annual statistical review, *Accident Facts.* The Council also provides films, slides, exhibits, and posters. The American National Red Cross, the American Automobile Association, various automobile and ammunition manufacturers, and many insurance companies also publish materials.

Medical, dental, nursing associations. Local doctors, dentists, and nurses and their professional associations take an active interest in school health education. The American Medical Association, Chicago, Illinois, has a department of health education which is staffed by consultants in school and public health education. The American Medical Association publishes *Today's Health* which can be used on the secondary school level. The Joint Committee on Health Problems in Education of the National Education Association and American Medical Association, which has functioned since 1911, provides vigorous leadership. Every administrator and health teacher should become familiar with the guidebooks and reports that the Joint Committee prepares (see bibliography, items 15, 16, 17, 18). The American Dental Association, Department of Dental Health Education, Chicago, Illinois, offers consultation services and has a list of its publication and audiovisual aids available free of charge. The American Nurses' Association and the National League for Nursing, New York, N.Y., also provide services.

Other organizations. A multiplicity of other associations, such as the National Health Council, New York, N.Y., and local and state health councils assist educators in many ways. One should not overlook the youth organizations such as the Boy Scouts, American Junior Red Cross, YMCA, YWCA, and Future Farmers of America. Many service clubs, labor unions, farm organizations, and social agencies also offer help. Space limitations make it impossible to list all of the organizations, their addresses, and the nature of their services. More complete information than is given below can be found in the *Encyclopedia of Associations,* Vol. I (see also bibliography, items 9, 11, 19, 24, 27).

Allied Youth Inc., (materials relating to temperance), 1346 Connecticut Ave., Suite 326, Washington 6, D.C.

American Academy of Pediatrics, 1801 Hinman Ave., Evanston, Illinois.

American Cancer Society, 521 W. 57th Street, New York 19, N.Y.

American Dietetics Association, 620 N. Michigan Avenue, Chicago, Illinois.

American Hearing Society, (*Hearing News*), 919 18th Street, N.W., Washington 6, D.C.

American Heart Association, 44 East 23rd St., New York 10, N.Y.

American Home Economics Association, (*Journal of Home Economics*), 1600 20th Street, N.W., Washington 9, D.C.

American Institute of Family Relations, (*Family Life*), 5287 Sunset Blvd., Los Angeles 27, California.

American National Red Cross, (materials relating to first aid, water safety, home nursing), 17th and D Street, N.W., Washington 6, D.C.

American Social Health Association, (*Social Hygiene News*), 1790 Broadway, New York 19, N.Y.

Association for Childhood Education—International, (*Childhood Education*), 3615 Wisconsin Ave., N.W., Washington 16, D.C.

Better Vision Institute, 230 Park Ave., New York 17, N.Y.

Bicycle Institute of America, 122 East 42nd St., New York, N.Y.

Central Council for Health Education, (*Health Education Journal*), Tavistock House, Tavistock Square, London, W.C. 1, England.

Child Study Association of America, (*Child Study*), 9 East 89th St., New York 28, N.Y.

Mental Health Materials Center, 104 East 25th St., New York 10, N.Y.

National Association for Mental Health, (*Understanding the Child; Mental Hygiene*), 10 Columbus Circle, New York 19, N.Y.

National Council on Alcoholism, 2 E-103rd Street, New York 29, N.Y.

National Congress of Parents and Teachers, (*National Parent-Teacher*), 700 N. Rush Street, Chicago 11, Illinois.

National Foot Health Council, 321 Union St., Rockland, Massachusetts.

National Foundation, (poliomyelitis, birth defects, arthritis), 800 2nd Street, New York 17, N.Y.

National Health Council, 1790 Broadway, New York 19, N.Y.

National Recreation Association, 8 W. 8th Street, New York 11, N.Y.

National Society for Crippled Children and Adults, Inc., 2023 W. Ogden Ave., Chicago 40, Illinois.

National Society for the Prevention of Blindness, Inc., (*Sight Saving Review*), 1790 Broadway, New York 19, N.Y.

National Tuberculosis Association, 1790 Broadway, New York 19, N.Y.

United Cerebral Palsy Association, 321 W. 44th St., New York 36, N.Y.

Universities, research centers, museums. Many universities offer graduate and undergraduate preparatory programs, workshops, and special conferences for health and safety educators and brief training programs for bus drivers, custodians, and food service employees. Sometimes professors in the fields of health and physical education, public health, education, medicine, dentistry, and home economics prepare health reports or publications for teachers. They may also provide local schools with technical assistance. Many colleges have established audiovisual aids centers, radio or television stations, and research centers. The Yale University Center of Alcohol Studies, the Center for Safety Education at New York University, the Iowa Child Welfare Station, and similar institutions do outstanding work and publish reports and journals that are of interest to teachers. The Cleveland Health Museum and some science museums display excellent health exhibits and also prepare materials for classroom use.

Commercial organizations. An abundance of attractive health education materials are produced by commercial concerns, insurance companies, and other special interest groups. From these sources teachers can often obtain teaching kits and guides, health units, pamphlets, films, film strips, posters, exhibits, models, and bibliographies. Many of these items are free and of excellent quality, but because some contain objectionable advertising or propaganda, all must be carefully screened:

Aetna Life Affiliated Companies, 151 Farmington Ave., Hartford 15, Connecticut.

American Automobile Association, 1712 G St., N.W., Washington, D.C.

American Seating Co. (posture posters), 9th and Broadway, Grand Rapids 2, Michigan.

Bristol-Myers Co., 630 Fifth Ave., New York 20, N.Y.

Cereal Institute, Inc., 135 South La Salle St., Chicago 3, Illinois.

Church and Dwight Co., Inc. (dental health), 70 Pine Street, New York 5, N.Y.

Employees Mutual of Wassau, 115 W. Wassau Ave., Wassau, Wisconsin.

Equitable Life Assurance Society of the United States, 393 Seventh Ave., New York 19, N.Y.

Florida Citrus Commission, Lakeland, Florida.

General Mills, Inc., Minneapolis 26, Minnesota.

International Cellucotton Products, Corp. (menstruation, colds), 919 N. Michigan Ave., Chicago 11, Illinois.

John Hancock Mutual Life Insurance Co., Boston 17, Massachusetts.

Johnson and Johnson Baby Products (first aid, safety), New Brunswick, N.J.

Kellogg Company, Department of Home Economics, Battle Creek, Michigan.

Kimberly-Clark Corporation, Educational Department (colds and menstruation), Neenah, Wisconsin.

Metropolitan Life Insurance Co., 1 Madison Ave., New York 10, N.Y.

National Dairy Council, 111 North Canal St., Chicago 6, Illinois.

National Board of Fire Underwriters, 85 John St., New York 38, N.Y.

Personal Products Corp. (menstruation), Milltown, N.J.

Prudential Insurance Company of America, Newark, N.J.

Remington Arms Company, Inc., Bridgeport 2, Connecticut.

Sonotone Corp., Professional Relations Department (hearing), Elmsford, N.Y.

Sunkist Growers, 707 W. 5th St., Los Angeles 17, California.

Sporting Arms and Ammunition Manufacturers Institute, 250 East 43rd St., New York 17, N.Y.

Tampax, Inc. (menstruation), 161 E. 42nd Street, New York 17, N.Y.

Travelers Insurance Company, Hartford, Connecticut.

United Fruit Company, Educational Service Department, New York 6, N.Y.

Wheat Flour Institute, 309 W. Jackson Blvd., Chicago 6, Illinois.

Numerous other commercial concerns also offer assistance. Some of these are American Can Company, Colgate-Palmolive Company, Borden Company, Continental Baking Company, General Electric Company, General Motors Corporation, Ford Motor Company,

Chrysler Corporation, H. J. Heinz Company, Lever Brothers Company, Maltex Company, and Proctor & Gamble.

Government agencies.   A health teacher should not overlook the invaluable resources offered by government agencies on various levels and the World Health Organization. The reports of WHO can be obtained from the Columbia University Press, International Documents Service, New York, N.Y.

Local level.   The local health department is a good source to turn to for advice and information. Upon request, medical health officers, public health nurses, laboratory technicians, or sanitary officers will usually help teachers. Many city health departments also employ public health educators, dentists, nutritionists, and other specialists who will assist in the schools. Members of the local fire, police, and recreation departments may also serve as resource personnel.

State level.   The state department of education may provide curriculum guides, reference lists of printed materials and audiovisual aids, and consultants. The state department of health may have several bureaus and laboratories that will supply films, statistics, bulletins, or reports. The state departments of conservation, recreation, and agriculture and the state police, corrective and mental institutions, and schools for the deaf and blind may also offer various types of assistance.

Federal level.   Three divisions of the United States Department of Health, Education, and Welfare render many services: (1) the Office of Education, which is most directly concerned with school problems, produces numerous reports that relate to health; provides consultant services; and publishes the journal, *School Life;* (2) the Public Health Service issues *Public Health Reports* and many other materials, houses the National Office of Vital Statistics (which produces the *Weekly Morbidity Report*), is responsible for the National Institutes of Health (a research center), and cooperates with local and state health agencies; and (3) the Children's Bureau publishes *The Child,* furnishes reports and statistics, and sponsors programs relating to child and maternal health, child labor, juvenile delinquency, and crippled children.

Another agency of the federal government that a health teacher may consult is the Bureau of Narcotics. The U.S. Department of Labor publishes materials on the health and safety of workers. The

U.S. Department of Agriculture supplies information on nutrition, family health, farm sanitation and safety, and its Bureau of Human Nutrition and Home Economics, extension agents, and 4-H club workers take an active interest in health problems.

A teacher can build a good library of health materials from government sources. He can obtain free copies of the biweekly listing, *Selected United States Government Publications,* and the annual price lists for specific topics from the U.S. Superintendent of Documents, Government Printing Office, Washington, D.C. The following lists may prove helpful: Price List 31, *Education* (see headings: Health and Physical Education and Recreation); Price Lists 41, 51, 51A, and 78 (health and safety topics); Price List 72, *Housing;* Price List 33A, *Vocations;* Price List 71, *Children.*

Evaluation and Collection of Materials

Because of the ever-increasing amount of health materials, teachers must evaluate them carefully and develop a systematic method of collecting and maintaining them.

Evaluation. The factors to consider when screening different types of resources vary, but, in general, the following questions should be raised:

1. Will the resource definitely aid in achieving the objectives of unit? Does it duplicate a previous experience pupils have had?
2. Are the illustrations, size of print, vocabulary, and concepts presented suitable for the age, intelligence, interests, and experiential background of the pupils?
3. Is the resource suitable for the size of the group and the type of community?
4. Does it have "eye, ear, and interest" appeal?
5. Is it sturdy, of good technical quality, and safe to use with children?
6. Are any useful supplementary aids provided, such as a teacher's guide, suggested activities, charts, graphs, and evaluative tools?
7. Does the cost, time consumption, or accessibility of the resource justify using it?
8. Does it contain objectionable propaganda or biases?
9. Is it scientifically accurate and up-to-date in content?
10. Will it actively involve pupils in emotional participation and critical thinking? Will it stimulate a high degree of self-activity?
11. Is the information presented and arranged so that it captures and holds pupils' attention, makes meanings clear, and provides a logical continuity of learning experiences?

12. Is all of the information pertinent and does it adequately cover what needs to be taught?

13. Does the material present new ideas and concepts but relate them to previous experiences and knowledges of youth so as to promote growth?

14. Does the publisher, author, producer, or speaker have a good reputation in the field?

15. Will this type of resource and specific item enable pupils to acquire the desired knowledge, attitude, or skill more quickly and effectively than any other resource that is available?

Resource centers and personal files.   Time, effort, and money can be saved if the school system establishes a central resource center in a special room or a library and appoints one or more persons to order, maintain, and issue items. The center's collection may consist of important health reference books, teaching methods books, periodicals, collections of textbooks and resource units, source materials from various agencies, bibliographies, catalogs and price lists, films, records, teaching kits, exhibit and demonstration materials, projectors, tape recorders, microscopes, models, charts, pictures, posters, specimens, and collections of books and pamphlets for children. The center may also establish a small health museum and have pupils cooperate in presenting exhibits.

Teachers can cooperate in compiling a card file that lists local agencies, plants, or areas that provide speakers, consultants, materials, or present worthwhile field trip possibilities. The cards may contain the following information: the type of resource, when and where it can be obtained or visited, the cost, special regulations that must be observed, information required when placing an order, name and telephone number of the person to contact, and travel information. After using a resource, notes may be added to indicate its value and how it could be used more effectively. Film evaluation files are also practical resource tools. Standardized forms for the file may be mimeographed and teachers can fill one out after using a film. A form may have blanks for the following information: title, producer, where it can be obtained, cost, sound or silent, color or black and white, running time, grade level, scientific accuracy, technical quality, student reactions, brief résumé, judgment concerning its merit, suggestions for using it in the future.

An instructor, of course, can gradually build up a private collection of free pamphlets, teaching aids, pictures, posters, photographs, and clippings and can compile lists of books, movies, and other resources for various health units. It may be possible for him to obtain funds for a small classroom library. If he makes notations on each teaching unit that indicate which resources and procedures were most successful, what pitfalls to avoid, and what new materials and suggestions might be tried next time, this will prove to be a valuable resource guide. If, when attending meetings, browsing in the library, or reading articles and books, he always carries cards on which to jot down the source, title, nature, cost, and merit of new resource materials, he can later give the cards suitable subject headings and alphabetize them. This will make it possible to relocate any item quickly. It is also wise for him to keep a copy of school policies concerning fields trips and various health and safety activities and services as well as personal lists of procedures that seem to work out best in various teaching situations.

CHAPTER VIII

Evaluation of Health and Safety Education

Evaluation in health and safety education embraces all phases of the program and is carried out on many levels and by many people. Evaluations may range from an informal appraisal of the work done by a pupil during an hour to a detailed study of the entire health program. In the latter case, a battery of evaluative techniques may be employed by committees organized on a state-, community-, system-, or schoolwide basis. The committees may consist of some or all of the following people: teachers, pupils, supervisors, administrators, health service staff members, parents, custodial and food service employees, and health workers in community and government agencies.

Evaluation begins with the initiation of a health education project, continues throughout the project, and does not necessarily terminate at its conclusion. Several steps are involved in the process. First, formal or informal appraisals are made to determine the present status. A check may be made of the available health services, facilities, and teaching materials. Pupils may be given health examinations and knowledge, attitude, and skill tests. These appraisals often arouse considerable staff and student interest in health problems. Moreover, they may convince pupils of their need for instruction and motivate them to work for improvements.

The information that is obtained from the evaluative tests, surveys, and inventories provide educators with helpful guideposts. It enables them to avoid duplicating what already has been done and reveals where they need to exert effort. It may help them determine what course content, methods, materials, facilities, staff members, or time allotments are needed. It may help them decide how to group pupils for instruction or how to counsel youngsters and their parents. Furthermore, the data provide bench marks for measuring future progress.

Evaluative techniques are also utilized to measure progress. After appraising present status data, instructors pinpoint specific objectives that need to be reached. Having done this, they select appropriate evaluative instruments for measuring the extent to which they achieve each objective. The participants informally appraise their work day-by-day and decide how to overcome weaknesses that are evident. From time to time they utilize their evaluative instruments to collect progress data.

At the conclusion of a project, the accumulated data is carefully analyzed to ascertain whether the health conditions and practices of the pupils, school, or community have improved as a result of the undertaking; whether errors or omissions need to be rectified; and what remains to be done. The body of progress data may reveal which methods, materials, curriculums, and teachers produced results and which did not. It may serve as a guide for planning future activities and for selecting instruments to determine the long-term effects of the program. It may be used as evidence to convince administrators or the public of the worth of the program.

Appraisal of the School Health Program

Educators utilize status and progress data to measure improvements in their program and pupils. Since the school health program consists of three interdependent parts—health instruction, healthful school living, and health services—each is appraised. Teams of outside experts, members of the school staff, and community workers may cooperate in doing this work, or any one of these groups or individuals may do it alone. They may evaluate all aspects of the program in one survey or they may confine their attention to different aspects at different times. A number of instruments are available to help evaluators make appraisals and lists of these are published occasionally in professional magazines.[1]

Total program. Some survey forms evaluate the scope and quality of several aspects of the school health program in terms of approved practices. Educators can construct these themselves or obtain them from state departments of education, universities, large

[1] Joint Committee on Evaluation: American Association for Health, Physical Education and Recreation; American Public Health Association; and American School Health Association, "Evaluation Instruments in School Health Education," *Journal of Health, Physical Education, and Recreation,* 26 (November, 1955), 13; and Joint Committee on Evaluation of School Health Programs, American Public Health Association, "Evaluate Your School Health Program," *Journal of School Health,* 26 (June, 1956), 166–74.

school systems, health agencies, or book publishers. An examination of materials such as the following can help them make decisions:

1. *A Checklist: Appraising the Elementary and Secondary School Health Program.* Bulletin 519. Austin, Texas: Texas Education Agency, 1951.

2. *A Check List for the Survey of Health and Physical Education Programs in Secondary Schools,* by Terry H. Dearborn. Stanford, California: Stanford University Press, 1951.

3. *A Check List of Safety and Safety Education in Your School.* Washington, D.C.: National Commission on Safety Education, National Education Association, 1953.

4. *Elementary School Health Education Program Inventory.* Sacramento, California: Elementary Evaluation Committee, School Health Education Evaluative Study, California State Department of Education, 1961.

5. "Evaluation of a Health Education Program," by Andie L. Knutson and Benjamin Shimberg. *American Journal of Public Health,* 45 (January, 1955), 21.

6. *Evaluation of School Health Education.* Albany, N.Y.: University of the State of New York, State Education Department, 1952.

7. *Evaluative Criteria.* Washington, D.C.: National Study of Secondary School Evaluation, American Council on Education, 1960.

8. *Health Education Evaluation Form,* by Charles Fast and Sara Williams. Portland, Oregon: Oregon Tuberculosis and Health Association.

9. *Health Evaluation Form.* Houston, Texas: Houston Public Schools, 1954.

10. *Health and Physical Education Score Card No. I, for Elementary Schools,* by William LaPorte. Los Angeles, California: Parker and Company.

11. *Health and Physical Education Score Card No. II, for Junior and Senior High Schools and Four Year High Schools,* by William LaPorte. Los Angeles, California: Parker and Company.

12. "Let's Rate Your Health Education Program," by C. O. Jackson, *Journal of Health, Physical Education, and Recreation,* 26 (September, 1955), 29.

13. *School Health Program Surveys.* Bloomington, Indiana: School of Health, Physical Education, and Recreation, Indiana University, 1956.

14. *School Health Education Evaluative Study, Los Angeles Area, 1954–1959, An Evaluation Research Study,* by Edward B. Johns. Los Angeles, California: University of California, 1960.

15. "School Health Program Evaluation Scale," *School Health Practice,* by C. L. Anderson. St. Louis, Missouri: C. V. Mosby Company, 1956, p. 485.

16. *Secondary School Health Education Program Inventory.* Sacra-

mento, California: Secondary Evaluation Committee, School Health Education Evaluative Study, California State Department of Education, 1961.

17. *Your Community: School-Community Fitness Inventory*. Washington, D.C.: National Education Association, American Association for Health, Physical Education, and Recreation, 1959.

School health instruction. In addition to the general survey evaluative forms, there are instruments that appraise specific aspects of the school health program. The following guides will help one evaluate factors relating to the instructional program:

1. "Evaluating Health Teaching," by H. Frederick Kilander. *Journal of Health, Physical Education, and Recreation,* 32 (November, 1961), 40.
2. "Evaluating Progress in Health Education," by Andie L. Knutson. *Journal of Health, Physical Education, and Recreation,* 28 (May–June, 1957), 21.
3. "Evaluation of Health Education Activities by Opinion Poll Techniques," by Oscar J. Kaplan. *American Journal of Public Health,* 41 (August, 1951), 31.
4. "Evaluation in the School Health Instruction Program," by J. H. Shaw. *American Journal of Public Health,* 47 (May, 1957), 582.
5. "Guide Posts for Evaluating Health Classes," by Bernice Moss. *Journal of Health, Physical Education, and Recreation,* 23 (March, 1952), 12.
6. *Health Teaching in Our Schools.* Albany, N.Y.: University of the State of New York, State Education Department, 1950.
7. *Pretesting: A Positive Approach to Evaluation,* by A. L. Knutson. *Public Health Reports,* 67, Washington, D.C.: USGPO (July, 1952).
8. *School Health Instruction Survey Form,* by W. P. Cushman. Columbus, Ohio: Ohio State University.

A national research project, The School Health Education Study, is now underway to improve the teaching of health in our schools.[2] The study is being financed by the Samuel Bronfman Foundation and is being conducted by the American Association for Health, Physical Education, and Recreation under the direction of Dr. Elena M. Sliepcevich.

To assess current health teaching status, the study staff is conducting a survey of the health instruction practices in a stratified random sampling of large, medium, and small school districts in

___
[2] "School Health Education Study, 1961–62," *Journal of Health, Physical Education, and Recreation,* 32 (January, 1962), 28.

the United States. A testing program is also being administered to a random sample group of students in Grades 6, 9, and 12 to measure the extent of their health knowledge and understanding. In addition, a number of outstanding health educators are preparing comprehensive bibliographies and a synthesis of research in several areas.

School health services.   To evaluate school health services, the teacher may use sections of the general survey instruments or some of the following guides:

1. "Appraisal Form for Evaluating School Health Services," *Journal of School Health,* 18 (January, 1948), 1.
2. *A Check List for School Health Services,* by H. R. Weatherbe. Stanford, California: Stanford University Press.
3. "Evaluating School Health Services," in *School Health Services.* Washington, D.C.: Joint Committee on Health Problems in Education of the National Education Association and the American Medical Association, 1953.
4. *Evaluation of Health Services in the School Health Program.* Jackson, Mississippi: State Board of Health and Department of Education, 1952.
5. *Health Appraisal of School Children,* 2nd ed. Washington D.C.: Joint Committee on Health Problems in Education of the National Education Association and American Medical Association, 1957.
6. *Health Services for the School-Age Child in Oregon.* Portland, Oregon: Oregon State Department of Education and State Board of Public Health, 1951.
7. Reports of the National Conferences on Physicians and Schools (held biennially) which are published by the American Medical Association, Bureau of Health Education, Chicago, Illinois.
8. "Suggested Standards for Health Services in Secondary Schools," *American Journal of Public Health Yearbook,* 42 (May, 1952).

Healthful school living.   To evaluate healthful school living, the teacher may use sections of the general survey instruments or some of the following guides:

1. "Appraising Healthful School Living," in *Healthful School Living.* Washington, D.C.: Joint Committee on Health Problems in Education of the National Education Association and American Medical Association, 1957.
2. *Check List for a Healthful and Safe School Environment.* Sacramento, California: Department of Education, 1957.
3. *Inspection and Supervision of the Health Aspects of the School Plant.* Sanitary Survey Form, Revision. Albany, N.Y.: State University

of New York, State Education Department, Division of Health and
Physical Education, 1948.

Appraisal of the Pupil

The school health program exists for one purpose: to bring about
improvements in the health knowledges, attitudes, interests, status,
and skills of children. A number of instruments have been devised
to appraise how successfully this is done. Some recently constructed
tools are cited in this chapter and additional items can be found in
bibliographies that appear in professional journals.[3] Some tests and
measurements books supply detailed descriptions of instruments
(see bibliography, items 4, 21, 30). Reports of efforts to construct
new ones appear in the *Research Quarterly, Journal of School
Health; Journal of Health, Physical Education, and Recreation;*
and similar journals.

Evaluation of knowledge. If youngsters are to improve their
health status and practices, they must acquire knowledge concerning the factors that contribute to mental and physical well-being and
must cultivate the capacity to think critically about health problems.

Published tests. A number of health knowledge tests have been
constructed by experts in the field. Many of them are standardized
tests. Directions and scoring keys are supplied and equivalent forms
are available that can be used as pre-tests and post-tests to measure
progress. Norms are also provided so that one can compare local
scores with those of large numbers of pupils:

1. *Bicycle Safety Quiz.* Information and Education Department, Hartford, Connecticut: Aetna Life Affiliated Companies. (Elementary Level)
2. *California Tests in Social and Related Sciences:* Part III, Related
Sciences, Test 5, *Health and Safety,* by Georgia S. Adams and J. A. Sex-
son. Monterey, California: California Test Bureau, 1953. (Grades 4–8)
3. *Community Bicycle Safety Program: What? Why? How?* New
York, N. Y.: Association of Casualty and Surety Companies, 1956.
4. *Elementary Health: Every Pupil Scholarship Test.* Emporia,
Kansas: Bureau of Educational Measurements, Kansas State Teachers
College, (Grades 6–8; Norms)
5. *Elementary Science and Health.* Columbus, Ohio: State Department of Education. (Grades 4, 5, 6; Norms)

---

[3] Marian K. Solleder, "Evaluation Instruments in Health Education," *Journal of
Health, Physical Education, and Recreation,* 32 (November, 1961), 42.

6. *Health Education Test: Knowledge and Application,* by John Shaw and Maurice Troyer. Rockville Centre, N.Y.: Acorn Publishing Company, 1956–57. (Grades 7–12; Norms)

7. *Health Education and Hygiene.* Columbus, Ohio: State Department of Education, biannually (Grades 7, 8, 9; Norms)

8. *Health and Safety Education Test,* by Lester Crow and Loretta Ryan. Rockville Centre, N.Y.: Acorn Publishing Company, 1960. (Grades 3–6; Norms)

9. *Health Test,* by Robert Speer and Samuel Smith. Rockville Centre, N.Y.: Acorn Publishing Company, (Form A) 1960, (Form B) 1957. (Grades 3–8)

10. *Kilander Health Knowledge Test: Evaluation and Adjustment Series.* (Write to H. F. Kilander, 33 Colonial Terrace, East Orange, N.J.) (Senior High School; Norms)

11. *Los Angeles Health Education Evaluation Instruments.* (Write to Dr. Blanche Bobbitt, Supervisor of Health Education, Box 3307, Terminal Annex, Los Angeles 54, California.) (Elementary and Secondary)

12. *Self-Quiz of Safety Knowledge,* by Joseph Dzenowagis. Chicago, Illinois: National Safety Council. (Grades 5 and 6)

13. *Sex Knowledge Inventory,* Form Y, by Gelolo McHugh. Durham, North Carolina: Family Life Publications, Inc., 1955. (Grades 9–12)

Teacher-made tests and appraisals. Published tests are not necessarily tailored to measure the specific knowledges that pupils in a given class are trying to master; hence, a teacher devises his own appraisal techniques for this purpose.

(1) ORAL QUESTIONS. By asking questions, the teacher can make some judgment concerning the knowledge that pupils possess. If the questions are carefully structured, the replies will reveal whether students are grasping ideas accurately, whether they can synthesize information and apply it in new situations, and where and why they are having difficulty. This question mode of appraisal is useful, but it has certain weaknesses: it is quite subjective, consumes considerable time, and cannot adequately sample the abilities of any one student. If the oral responses are not recorded, they cannot be re-examined for evaluation at a later date. Because of variation in the difficulty of the questions, it is impossible to compare the achievements of different pupils. Moreover, variations in pupils' ability to express themselves orally and in their emotional stability may affect the appraisals.

(2) EXAMPLES OF WORK.   An instructor can make judgments about pupils' health knowledge and ability to apply it by examining their work. Notebooks, reports, and other projects that are done outside of school hours do not absorb class time, but they may not have been done independently. The teacher's appraisal of work that is done in or out of class may be quite subjective and may give consideration to factors other than knowledge, such as ability to write, draw, or act.

(3) ESSAY TESTS.   Essay tests can help one assess depth and clarity of understanding. This is particularly true if the questions present problem-situations rather than merely calling for the reproduction of specific facts. Good essay questions require pupils to note relationships or to apply, interpret, explain, or evaluate information.

Essay tests have one major limitation: the scoring is quite subjective and time-consuming. Moreover, the tests can only assess a limited sampling of a student's knowledge, and factors other than knowledge—such as handwriting or ability in composition—may be given consideration in the appraisal. These handicaps can be somewhat overcome, however, if the teacher increases the number of questions, limits the length of the replies, and asks questions that clearly indicate the specific areas to be discussed. Greater objectivity in scoring can be achieved if certain precautions are taken. Before grading a test, the teacher might write out the answers and assign to each one a scoring weight. When correcting tests, it is best to score one question at a time on all papers and to do it without noting the writers of the responses.

(4) COMPLETION TEST.   An overemphasis on the memorization of factual data is objectionable, but a mastery of some facts is essential. Completion tests are suitable instruments for measuring this type of knowledge. They are composed of questions or incomplete statements and require pupils to supply the missing specific items of information. Completion tests are easy to construct and they minimize the possibility of "guessing." They are easier to score than essay questions and provide a more comprehensive coverage of materials in a limited time. The scoring of such questions is more subjective and difficult, however, than the scoring of selection-type test questions.

(5) SELECTION-TYPE TEST. True-false, multiple-choice, and matching test items require pupils to select correct answers from alternatives given. Pupils do not have to supply information, and no direct assessment is made of their ability to explain, to give reasons for, or to name. Since correct answers can be attained by guessing, the tests do not necessarily reveal pupils' strengths and weaknesses. Selection-type tests do have some definite advantages: they can obtain a wide sampling of knowledge in a relatively short time, and they can be scored with ease and with complete objectivity.

When composing selection-type tests, the teacher must avoid ambiguity and refrain from using word or pattern clues that indicate the correct answer (such as making all odd-numbered statements true). When possible, the teacher should reword principles or present concepts in new situations so that pupils have to apply what they have learned rather than merely identify what they have memorized or seen in a book. In general, multiple-choice items are considered to be more effective than true-false and matching items, but they are also the most difficult to construct.

Evaluation of interests and attitudes. Youngsters learn when they are genuinely interested in a health problem and apply what they learn if they develop a favorable attitude toward the practice. Hence, to bring about desirable long-term health behavior, an instructor must possess information about both the interests and attitudes of pupils. Some research studies have been conducted that provide information about children's health interests.[4] If students are given a long list of health topics, they can check those they would like to study. If they are encouraged to submit anonymous questions about health problems that concern them, they may reveal information that might otherwise remain concealed. During a unit, an instructor can make some judgments about the intensification and broadening of interests by noting the questions that pupils ask, the materials they bring to class, the library books they read, and the comments their parents make. When interest in a unit seems to lag, an informal class discussion may pinpoint the causes.

Health attitudes are difficult to define, measure, and appraise ob-

---

[4] Denver Public Schools, *Health Interests of Children; a Report of a Research Study*, rev. ed. (Denver, Colorado: Board of Education, 1954); and Joseph E. Lantagne, "Health Interests of 10,000 Secondary Students," *Research Quarterly*, 23 (October, 1952), 330–46.

jectively, for they are rooted in the private, emotional world of the individual and are subject to change. A person's actions may not always reflect his feelings accurately. Johnny may donate to a health drive because of group pressure rather than because he believes in the worth of the project. Real changes in attitudes are apt to take place slowly. Moreover, it is difficult to distinguish whether one is measuring pupils' real attitudes or their knowledge of correct social responses. Consequently, there are few health attitude instruments available and many of these measure knowledge about attitudes rather than real attitudes. Some of the evaluative instruments that have been devised are:

1. *Byrd Health Attitude Scale.* Stanford, California: Stanford University Press, 1940. (High school and College)
2. *Health Knowledge and Attitude Test,* by Vera Getchell. Topeka, Kansas: Bureau of Educational Measurements, Kansas State Teachers College, 1947. (Grades 4–8)
3. "A Health and Safety Attitude Scale for the Seventh Grade," by Cyrus Mayshark. *Research Quarterly,* 27 (March, 1956), 52.
4. *"A Safety Attitude Scale for the Seventh Grade,"* by Frank Myers. *Research Quarterly,* 29 (October, 1958), 320.

To a large extent, a teacher relies on subjective methods of assessing attitudes and interests. To obtain evidence, he observes pupils' behavior and notes their remarks in casual conversations, interviews, classes, play situations, club meetings, the cafeteria, hallways, and the streets. In general, the more systematic and specific his observations are, the more useful and reliable are his data. Occasionally, he may ask students to name classmates that they would like to work or play with and construct a sociogram to ascertain their attitudes toward one another and to spot shifts in interpersonal relationships. When a youngster presents a puzzling problem, teachers and specialists in the field may conduct a detailed case study to obtain an integrated picture of his past experiences, present status, and relationships in the home-school-community. This information places them in a better position to help the youngster.

Evaluation of skills. Health skills consist of two important elements: a knowledge of the correct procedures to use and the ability to perform the skill correctly. To evaluate the former, a teacher uses health knowledge tests. When appraising the latter, he directly observes the pupil demonstrate a skill, such as home nursing, first aid, water safety, bicycle riding, or automobile driving. Agencies such as the American National Red Cross, National Safety Council, and various insurance companies supply some skill tests. A teacher can construct his own by listing the specific items to note and deciding what weight is to be given to various aspects of the skill.

    Evaluation of status and practices. Two primary questions that educators seek to answer are: (1) Has the health status of pupils changed for the better as a result of the school health program? (2) To what extent do pupils apply the health knowledge that they study? Hence, instructors collect data that will enable them to make comparisons between a pupil's present and past health status and practices, between the status of different groups of youngsters, and between a pupil's individual status and that which is considered acceptable for his age group.

    The health service personnel assumes the responsibility for appraising the health status of pupils, but teachers often participate in conducting screening tests. To test vision, they may use one of the Snellen test charts, the Massachusetts Vision Test, or tests that make use of a telebinocular machine. To assess hearing, they may use the watch-tick test, forced whisper test, or audiometer tests. To ascertain whether growth is proceeding satisfactorily, they may check pupils' height and weight and other body measurements. A crude measure of status can be found by using height-weight-age tables. It is not advisable to place too much reliance upon these tables, however, because they fail to take into account differences in proportions of skeletal build, amount of fat, and muscular development. A more accurate appraisal of status can be attained by using one of the following methods of measurement: the Wetzel Grid, Meredith Physical Growth Records, Pryor Width-Weight Tables, or ACH Index of Nutritional Status.

    To obtain information about health screening tests, the teacher can consult teaching methods books (see bibliography, items 11, 27, 28) and tests and measurements books (see bibliography, items 4, 21, 30). The latter give detailed information about body measurement techniques, motor fitness tests, strength tests, motor ability tests, posture and foot measurements, and other screening tests.

    Cumulative records provide a valuable reservoir of data that an instructor can draw upon to assess pupils' health status. From this source he can find out what progress pupils are making in correcting their physical defects and solving their previous health problems, what new problems they are encountering, and which pupils need examinations and treatment by qualified specialists. When studying the data, the teacher should endeavor to discover not only where progress is lagging, but also what is hampering it and what can be done or should have been done to bring about better results. Among other reports that he can examine to appraise the effectiveness of the health education program are the school accident reports, cafeteria records of milk and food sales, health and safety survey reports, library withdrawal records of health books, and vital statistics from the health department.

Through informal daily observations, the teacher can appraise many aspects of pupils' health: posture, personal cleanliness, relationships with classmates, how they dress for various weather conditions, whether they wear their glasses, their emotional and physical adjustments to non-remedial defects, and any signs of developing illnesses or deviations from normal appearance or behavior.[5] Writing brief anecdotal records of things that pupils do or say from time to time provides an instructor with subjective evidence of changes that are taking place. When this is done, it is important to record instances of good behavior as well as those of undesirable behavior.

An instructor can obtain much information about pupils and local health problems by asking questions in private interviews or in group discussions and by utilizing structured inventories, checklists, surveys, and questionnaires. If pupils supply the same type of information periodically, an estimate can be made of their progress. Among the published instruments that are available are:

1. *Health Behavior Inventory to Evaluate Health Behavior in the Senior High School,* by E. Harold Le Maistre. Monterey, California: California Test Bureau, Del Monte Research Park, 1958.

2. *Health Inventory for High School Students,* by Gerwin Neher. Monterey, California: California Test Bureau, Del Monte Research Park, 1942. (Grades 9–12)

3. *Health Practice Inventory,* by Edward Johns and Warren Juhnke. Stanford, California: Stanford University Press, 1952. (High school and college levels; norms)

---

[5] James F. Rogers, "What Every Teacher Should Know About the Physical Condition of Her Pupils." Pamphlet No. 68 (Washington, D.C.: USGPO, 1955); and G. M. Wheatley and G. T. Hallock, *Health Observations of School Children,* 2nd ed. (New York: McGraw-Hill Book Company, Inc., 1956).

4. *A Health Practice Inventory for Children in Grades Three, Four, and Five,* by Sylvia Yellen. Monterey, California: California Test Bureau, Del Monte Research Park, 1957.

If pupils are allowed to help establish standards for desirable health practices and help construct some of the appraisal instruments, the evaluation process will be more meaningful to them. Keeping growth, food, and daily schedule records and rating their personal appearance, table manners, and bicycle safety practices can generate considerable interest in seeking improvements. Self-evaluation, combined with appraisals by their classmates, is also helpful.

Teachers can construct their own checklists to insure that they do not overlook important factors when observing pupils. They can also prepare questionnaires for pupils and parents to fill out. To obtain meaningful and accurate data, the instruments must be carefully structured and administered. Questions that are asked of very young pupils should refer to specific and recent practices. It is better to ask "What did you eat for breakfast this morning?" than to ask "What do you generally or usually eat for breakfast?" When administering these instruments, it is important to inform the respondents that the objective is to obtain information concerning what they do, not what they know. They should also be told that the instruments are not tests and that their responses will not influence their marks. In many instances it is better to have students reply anonymously or to assure them that their responses will be kept confidential.

During the past century, establishing health and safety programs, determining what to teach, and obtaining qualified personnel absorbed most of the time and energy of educators. Today, society is sharply scrutinizing our schools. To meet the current demands for more effective and economical educational programs, health and safety teachers must expand and improve the evaluation activities. This makes it imperative for research workers to probe more deeply into existing evaluation theories and practices, to refine some of the instruments and techniques that have been developed, and to create new and better ones.

Bibliography

1. American Association of School Administrators, *Health in Schools*. Twentieth Yearbook. Washington, D.C.: National Education Association, 1951.

2. Anderson, Carl L., *School Health Practice*. St. Louis, Missouri: C. V. Mosby Company, 1960.

3. Association for Supervision and Curriculum Development, *Fostering Mental Health in Our Schools*. Washington, D.C.: National Education Association, 1950.

4. Clarke, H. Harrison, *Application of Measurement to Health and Physical Education*. Englewood Cliffs, N.J.: Prentice-Hall, Inc., 1959.

5. Committee on School Health Policies, *Suggested School Health Policies*. Washington, D.C. and Chicago: National Education Association and American Medical Association, 1956.

6. Department of Elementary School Principals, "The Elementary School Health Program," *National Elementary Principal*, 39 (February, 1960), 1–48.

7. Diehl, Harold S. and S. C. Thomson, *Textbook of Healthful Living*. New York: McGraw-Hill Book Company, Inc., 1960.

8. Florio, A. E. and G. T. Stafford, *Safety Education*. New York: McGraw-Hill Book Company, Inc., 1962.

9. Grout, Ruth E., *Health Teaching in Schools*. Philadelphia: W. B. Saunders Company, 1958.

10. Haag, Jessie H., *School Health Program*. New York: Holt, Rinehart & Winston, Inc., 1958.

11. Harnett, Arthur L. and John H. Shaw, *Effective School Health Education*. New York: Appleton-Century-Crofts, Inc., 1959.

12. Hein, Fred V., "Health Education," *Encyclopedia of Educational Research*. New York: The Macmillan Company, 1960.

13. Humphrey, James H., W. R. Johnson, and V. D. Moore, *Elementary School Health Education*. New York: Harper & Row, Publishers, 1962.

14. Irwin, Leslie W., James H. Humphrey, and Warren R. Johnson, *Methods and Materials in School Health Education*. St. Louis, Missouri: The C. V. Mosby Company, 1956.

15. Joint Committee on Health Problems in Education of the National Education Association and the American Medical Association, *Health Education*. Washington, D.C.: National Education Association, 1961.

16. ———. *Healthful School Living.* Washington, D.C.: National Education Association, 1957.

17. ———. *Health Appraisal of School Children.* Washington, D.C.: National Education Association, 1957.

18. ———. *School Health Services.* Washington, D.C.: National Education Association and American Medical Association, 1954.

19. Kilander, H. Frederick, *School Health Education.* New York: The Macmillan Company, 1962.

20. Langton, C. V. and C. L. Anderson, *Health Principles and Practice.* St. Louis, Missouri: The C. V. Mosby Company, 1953.

21. Meyers, Carlton R. and T. Erwin Blesh, *Measurement in Physical Education.* New York: The Ronald Press Company, 1962.

22. Nemir, Alma, *School Health Program.* Philadelphia: W. B. Saunders Company, 1959.

23. Oberteuffer, Delbert, *School Health Education.* New York: Harper & Row, Publishers, 1960.

24. Schneider, Robert E., *Methods and Materials of Health Education.* Philadelphia: W. B. Saunders Company, 1958.

25. Smith, Helen N. and Mary E. Wolverton, *Health Education in the Elementary School.* New York: The Ronald Press Company, 1959.

26. Stack, Herbert J. and J. Duke Elkow, *Education for Safe Living.* Englewood Cliffs, N.J., Prentice-Hall, Inc., 1957.

27. Turner, C. E., C. Morley Sellery, and Sara L. Smith, *School Health and Health Education.* St. Louis, Missouri: The C. V. Mosby Company, 1961.

28. Wheatley, George M. and Grace T. Hallock, *Health Observations of School Children.* New York: McGraw-Hill Book Company, Inc., 1956.

29. Willgoose, Carl E., *Health Education in the Elementary School.* Philadelphia: W. B. Saunders Company, 1959.

30. ———. *Evaluation in Health Education and Physical Education.* New York: McGraw-Hill Book Company, Inc., 1961.

Index

Index